LAMDA
VERSE AND PROSE
ANTHOLOGY

Volume 18

The LAMDA *Verse and Prose Anthology (Volume 18)*

First published in 2014 by the London Academy of Music and Dramatic Art
155 Talgarth Road, London W14 9DA, United Kingdom
Tel: +44 (0)844 847 0520 / Fax: +44 (0)844 847 0521
www.lamda.org.uk

A catalogue record for this book is available from the British Library.

Printed by: CPI Group (UK) Ltd, Croydon, CR0 4YY
Cover image: Ann Pownall Photography
Concept design and layout: Cambridge Design Consultants

ISBN: 9780955768767

The LAMDA *Verse and Prose Anthology (Volume 18)* is a collection of verse and prose and is a required publication for learners taking LAMDA *Graded Examinations in Communication: Speaking Verse and Prose* and the LAMDA *Introductory Examinations Stage One, Stage Two and Stage Three (Solo and Group)*.

You may notice that in the case of certain poems or prose extracts, spelling of some words may vary from piece to piece, representing either standard British or American spelling. This is because we have maintained the spelling found in the original source material.

Contents

Contents *continued*

Contents *continued*

▼ Level 3 Speaking Verse and Prose: Grade 8 Verse

▼ Level 3 Speaking Verse and Prose: Grade 8 Prose

Introduction

The spoken word has the power to inspire, excite and even transform lives. Whether shared through the medium of verse or prose, it can transport both performer and audience into new worlds of literary discovery.

Since 1950, LAMDA's examinations have provided readers with the opportunity to embark on such a journey, encouraging the performance of both verse and prose. This is the eighteenth *Verse and Prose Anthology* produced by LAMDA.

In this anthology, younger learners are introduced to characters from literary classics such as *Through the Looking-Glass* and *William in Trouble*, as well as being introduced to more contemporary figures like *Fantastic Mr Fox, Mr Gum* and *Coraline*. They can explore word pictures in poetry about a *New Day*, a *Dragonfly* or *Winter Trees* as well as enjoying the humour of the *Big Fat Budgie* and *The Cats' Protection League*.

Images, concepts and more complex storylines develop as the grades progress and older learners have the opportunity of discovering great classic authors such as Jane Austen, Charles Dickens, F Scott Fitzgerald and Sir Arthur Conan Doyle as well as newer writers from a variety of cultures, such as Michael Ondaatje and Khaled Hosseini. This breadth is extended to poetry, where learners are introduced to the word worlds of Christina Rossetti, Henry Wadsworth Longfellow, Siegfried Sassoon and Ted Hughes as well as exciting new poetry from the South African poet Katharine Kilalea, the Sudanese Al-Saddiq Al-Raddi and the Iranian-British Mimi Khalvati. Poetry speaks from the heart to the heart, and the traveller through the final pages of this anthology will experience poetic worlds describing the problems faced by refugees, the horrors of war and effects of terrorism, as well as enjoying light-hearted glimpses of young children, old age and strange characters on a medieval pilgrimage.

It is an anthology of both variety and vitality. I hope you will find some of the work memorable and all of it enjoyable.

Carol Ann Duffy (CBE)

UK Poet Laureate

Thanks

LAMDA would like to thank all of the authors, publishers and agents who made the development of this anthology possible. Special thanks are also due to Clarissa Aykroyd, Paul Bench, Jacque Emery, Jeffrey Grenfell-Hill and Ann Newson.

Solo Introductory

Stage One

Titles in Solo Introductory Stage One

On the Beach

They buried their dad
in the golden sands,
buried his legs,
buried his hands,
buried his body
and buried his toes
and left just his face
and a very red nose.

by Marian Swinger

This Tooth

I jiggled it
  jaggled it
  jerked it.

I pushed
  and pulled
  and poked it.

But –

As soon as I stopped,
And left it alone,
This tooth came out
On its very own!

by Lee Bennett Hopkins

New Day

The day is so new
You can hear it yawning,
Listen:

The new day
is yawning
and stretching

and waiting to start.

In the clear blue sky
I hear the new day's heart.

by Ian McMillan

The Dragonfly

When the heat of the summer
Made drowsy the land,
A dragonfly came
And sat on my hand,
With its blue jointed body,
And wings like spun glass,
It lit on my fingers
As though they were grass.

by Eleanor Farjeon

The Falling Star

I saw a star slide down the sky,
Blinding the north as it went by,
Too burning and too hot to hold,
Too lovely to be bought or sold,
Good only to make wishes on
And then forever to be gone.

by Sara Teasdale

A Lion

A lion in a zoo,
Shut up in a cage,
Lives a life
Of smothered rage.

A lion in the plain,
Roaming free,
Is happy as ever
A lion can be.

by Langston Hughes

Group Introductory

Stage One

Titles in Group Introductory Stage One

Ghost Hunting

Ssh!
It's dark
Don't giggle or shout!
Just keep still,
There's a ghost about!
Down in the cellar,
Look with care,
There's a cold wind moaning,
Beware......beware
He rattles the shelves,
He moves the bed,
He breaks the glasses
And stains the mat red!
Ooh – look out,
It's coming in here,
Closer and closer,
......and CLOSER, I fear.
Help! Help!
Let's get out!
I'm scared; I feel sick!
Let's go while we can,
Hurry up! Quick!

It's still now, the house.
Not one stray, nosy peep!
Thank goodness that's over –
This ghost wants to sleep!

by Jacqueline Emery

Hamburgers

Hamburgers big and Hamburgers small,
Hamburgers pictured and hung on the wall,
Hamburgers jolly and round and fat,
Hamburgers domed like a bowler hat,
Hamburgers served with onion and cheese,
Hamburgers trying their hardest to please,
Hamburgers saucy and Hamburgers plain,
Hamburgers hearty in sunshine or rain,
Hamburgers plump and Hamburgers tall,
The people of Hamburg are Hamburgers all.

by Colin Thiele

What a Racket!

Once upon a time,
We lived in a house in town
And
THE CATS MIAOWED,
THE DOGS BOW-WOWED,
THE COLD WIND HOWLED,
THE LORRIES ROARED,
THE AIRCRAFT SOARED,
THE WINDOWS RATTLED
AND THE THUNDER CRASHED.

"The trouble with living in *town*," said Mum,
"is that it is SO noisy."
So we moved to the country –
And
THE CATS MIAOWED,
THE DOGS BOW-WOWED,
THE SHEEP WENT BAA,
THE COWS WENT MOO,
THE TRACTORS CHUGGED,
THE COLD WIND BLEW,
THE THUNDER CRASHED,
THE FIELD MICE SQUEAKED,
THE RAIN POURED DOWN,
THE HOUSE ROOF LEAKED.
"Lovely!" said Mum.
"There's nothing quite like *country* sounds!"

by Trevor Harvey

Solo Introductory

Stage Two

Big Fat Budgie

I'm a big fat budgie,
  I don't do a lot.
Might park on my perch.
    Might peck in my pot.
          Might peek at my mirror.
    Might ring my bell.
Might peer through the bars of my fat budgie cell.
        Might say "Who's a pretty boy then?"
          Might not.
I'm a big fat budgie.
  I don't do a lot.

by Michaela Morgan

My Card for Father's Day

This is the card that I've made for my dad.
It's sticky with glue… but it's not too bad.

I cut out this ship and then stuck it in
And I drew this shark with a great big fin.

Then I've written as neatly as I can
"With love to my dad. He's the world's best man!"

This is the card that I'll give to my dad.
It's sticky with glue… but it's not too bad.

by Wes Magee

The Vulture

The Vulture eats between his meals,
    And that's the reason why
He very, very rarely feels
    As well as you or I.
His eye is dull, his head is bald,
    His neck is growing thinner.
Oh, what a lesson for us all
    To only eat at dinner.

by Hilaire Belloc

Until I Saw the Sea

Until I saw the sea
I did not know
that wind
could wrinkle water so.

I never knew
that sun
could splinter a whole sea of blue.

Nor
did I know before,
a sea breathes in and out
upon a shore.

by Lilian Moore

My Sari

Saris hang on the washing line:
a rainbow in our neighbourhood.
This little orange one is mine,
it has a mango leaf design.
I wear it as a Rani would.
It wraps around me like sunshine,
it ripples silky down my spine,
and I stand tall and feel so good.

by Debjani Chatterjee

Winter Trees

Aren't you cold and won't you freeze,
With branches bare, you winter trees?
You've thrown away your summer shift,
Your autumn gold has come adrift.

Dearie me, you winter trees,
What strange behaviour if you please!
In summer, you could wear much less,
But come the winter, you undress!

by Zoltán Zelk,
translated by George Szirtes from the Hungarian

Group Introductory

Stage Two

Titles in Group Introductory Stage Two

Where Teachers Keep Their Pets

Mrs Cox has a fox
Nesting in her sweaty socks.

Mr Spratt's tabby cat
Sleeps beneath his bobble hat.

Miss Cahoots has various newts
Swimming in her zip-up boots.

Mr Spry has Fred his fly
Eating food stains off his tie.

Mrs Groat shows off her stoat
Round the collar of her coat.

Mr Spare's got grizzly bears
Hiding in his spacious flares.

And...

Mrs Vickers... has a stick insect called Stickers
And she keeps it in her...

by Paul Cookson

The Mutinous Jack-in-the-box

Why should I always jump up
when they press that stupid button
always at their call?
Next time... *next* time...
I'll stick my tongue out at them!
I'll spit!
I'll shout rude words!
I'll pull horrid faces!
I'll make their baby cry
and turn their milk sour;
I will!
Just you wait and see!
They can't fool me;
not for ever a slave;
next time I'll be brave.

B o o o o o o o o o o o i i i i i i i i i n n n n n n n g g g !

Oh dear, I jumped up again,
Grinning as though I had no brain.
But... just you wait and see,
Next time I'll do it;
I will... I will...

by John Cunliffe

Chinese New Year in China Town

It's New Year's Day
in China Town,
another year
is counted down.

Fireworks shoot
showers of light
lanterns wave,
burning bright.

Children dance
in the crowd,
smiling faces
cheer out loud.

Dragons twist
up and down,
for it's New Year's Day
in China Town.

by Andrew Collett

Solo Introductory

Stage Three

Titles in Solo Introductory Stage Three

The Little Ghost's Song

I'd like to be human again.
I'd like to get wet in the rain.
I wouldn't mind toothache
Just for living's sake!
I'd like to get wet in the rain.
I'd like to be human again.
I'd like to kick a ball
And my foot not go through at all!
What's the good of being a ghost
If you can't eat jam and toast?
If you can't pull a funny face,
Or be sent to bed in disgrace?
I'd rather be scared than scare,
I'd like to breathe some air.
I'd like to get wet in the rain.
I'd love to be human again!

by Brian Patten

Farewell, Pete

I had a little dinosaur
Nothing would it eat
But a chocolate cupcake
And my best mate, Pete

At school it burst the football
It wasn't fond of sports
It gobbled up the goalposts
and Mr Walton's shorts

It chased my Auntie Emma
You should have heard her shout
But it didn't like my granny
In fact, it spat her out

by Roger Stevens

Is the Moon Tired?

Is the moon tired? She looks so pale
Within her misty veil;
She scales the sky from east to west,
And takes no rest.

Before the coming of the night
The moon shows papery white;
Before the dawning of the day
She fades away.

by Christina Rossetti

City Jungle

Here I am
In the jungle city.
Tigers, like cars
Chase our feet.
Wild birds,
Like children
Scream bitterly.
Elephants lumber around
Like buses,
Giraffes have necks
As tall as buildings
And the monkeys' chatter
Sounds like my sister's.

by Nicole Townsend

The Door

A white door in a hawthorn hedge –
Who lives through there?
A sorcerer? A wicked witch
With serpents in her hair?

A king enchanted into stone?
A lost princess?
A servant girl who works all night
Spinning a cobweb dress?

A queen with slippers made of ice?
I'd love to see.
A white door in a hawthorn hedge –
I wish I had a key.

by Richard Edwards

Ballet Lesson

They've sent me to ballet,
Yes honestly – me!
With two left feet
And a graze on my knee.
They've given me pink shoes,
All satin and smooth,
I'd prefer trainers,
But I couldn't choose.
My leotard is mauve,
I look like a plum.
Ballet's not a good idea
And I wish I hadn't come.

by Eleanor McLeod

Group Introductory

Stage Three

Titles in Group Introductory Stage Three

Midnight Cats

Meooww......pssssss......
Scratching,
Leaping,
Clawing,
Dashing,
Streaks of silver
Flashing by the streetlamp.
Prowling,
Snarling,
Darting,
Crashing,
Dustbin lids
Clattering down below.
Hissing,
Screeching,
Yowling,
Tearing,
Balls of fur
Rolling with a loud crash!
Arching,
Sleeking,
Proudly
Retreating –
Battle over
For the midnight cats.
Meooww.........pssssssssss.

by Jacqueline Emery

Question Time

What does a monster look like?
Well… hairy and scary,
   and furry and burly
      and pimply and dimply
        and warty
         and naughty
           and wrinkled and crinkled…
That's what a monster looks like.

How does a monster move?
It oozes.
   It shambles.
      It crawls and it ambles.
        It slouches and shuffles
         and trudges.
It lumbers and waddles,
   it creeps and it toddles…
That's how a monster moves.

Where does a monster live?
In garden sheds,
   under beds,
      in wardrobes,
        in plug holes,
         in ditches.
Beneath city streets,
      just under your feet…
That's where a monster lives.

How does a monster eat?
It slurps
        and it burps.
            It gobbles and gulps.
                It sips and it swallows
                    and scoffs.
                It nibbles and munches.
                    It chews and it crunches.
That's how a monster eats.

What does a monster eat?
Slugs.
    And bats.
        And bugs
            and rats.
                And stones and mud
                    and bones and blood.
And squelchy squids…
                and nosy kids.
YUM!
That's what a monster eats!

by Michaela Morgan

A Football Game

It's the might, it's the fight
  Of two teams who won't give in –
It's the roar of the crowd
  And the "Go, fight, win!"

It's the bands, it's the stands,
  It's the color everywhere.
It's the whiff, it's the sniff
  Of the popcorn on the air.
It's a thrill, it's a chill,
  It's a cheer and then a sigh;
It's that deep, breathless hush
  When the ball soars high.

Yes, it's more than a score,
  Or a desperate grasp at fame;
Fun is King, win or lose –
  That's a football game!

by Alice Van Eck

Entry 3 Speaking Verse and Prose

Entry Level

It Wasn't Me

It wasn't me, my cup just fell,
The plate jumped on the floor,
The window cracked all by itself
And then it slammed the door.

I didn't punch, my hand just slipped
And curled into a fist.
He happened to come walking by,
I happened not to miss.

It wasn't me who talked in class,
I didn't steal that pen,
If someone says they saw me cheat
They've got it wrong again.

It wasn't me, it's not my fault!
Why do I get the blame?
The naughty child who does these things
Has pinched my face and name.

by Steve Turner

The Spangled Pandemonium

The spangled pandemonium
Is missing from the zoo.
He bent the bars the barest bit,
And slithered glibly through.

He crawled across the moated wall,
He climbed the mango tree,
And when the keeper scrambled up,
He nipped him in the knee.

To all of you, a warning
Not to wander after dark,
Or if you must, make very sure
You stay out of the park.

For the spangled pandemonium
Is missing from the zoo,
And since he nipped his keeper,
He would just as soon nip you.

by Palmer Brown

Peacock

I sit and watch a silver blotch
On yonder lonely hill
The tinkling air grows grey and bare,
The wind blows wet and chill.

The peacock dons his blue and bronze
And under the falling shower
Spreads out his plumes and swiftly blooms
To an enamelled flower.

by Harindranath Chattopadhyaya

Snake

Snake slithers
  among stones
    coils and loops
      and hisses
    forked tongue
  darts as fast
as an arrow,
  aims and misses.

Snake glides
  over pebbles,
    sleeps, snoozing
      in the sun,
    hunger long-
  forgotten,
waits still, till
  day is done.

by Moira Andrew

Chicken Poxed

My sister was spotty,
Real spotty all over,
She was plastered with spots
From her head to her toes.

She had spots on the parts
That her bathing suits cover,
Spots on her eyelids,
Spots on her nose.

I didn't know chickenpox
Could be so interesting,
It seemed such a shame
To waste all those spots.

So when Jody was sleeping
And no one was looking,
I got a blue pen
And connected her dots.

by Valerie Bloom

Night Spinner

A spider spinning her web one night
Wove in some silver starlight bright
Then caught some drops
Of moon-washed rain
And threaded them
Into a crystal chain.

Crystal and silver
Crystal and silver
Laced between leaves
On the autumn trees.

Silver and crystal
Silver and crystal
Shivering
Shimmering
In the dawn breeze.

by Patricia Leighton

Sunday Tea

A small but hairy alien
came to our house for tea.
He shook hands most politely,
put his napkin on his knee.

We found his table manners, though,
were really rather bad.
Despite his size, his mouth was huge
enough to eat my dad.

He scoffed my baby sister
then he gorged himself on mother.
He choked a little at the taste
of my revolting brother.

He slobbered as he gulped them down
and gave a belch or two,
and as he swallowed each of them
his belly swelled and grew.

A massive hairy alien
enjoyed his Sunday tea.
Oh dear, I think I'll have to run…
he's reaching out for me.

by Alison Chisholm

Grandfather Frog

Fat green frog sits by the pond,
Big frog, bull frog, grandfather frog.
Croak – croak – croak
Shuts his eye, opens his eye,
Rolls his eye, winks his eye
Waiting for
A little fat fly.
Croak, croak.
I go walking down by the pond,
I want to see the big green frog.
I want to stare right into his eye.
Rolling, winking, funny old eye.
But oh! he hears me coming by.
Croak – croak –
SPLASH!

by Louise Bechtel

Level 1 Speaking Verse and Prose

Grade 1

Titles in Level 1 Speaking Verse and Prose: Grade 1

The Last Dragon

By a dusk-damp cave
As the first snows fall
A dragon breathes;
The last of them all.

His eyes are dull,
His memories old;
His breath is pale,
His fire now cold.

The forest mice
Who ran from his roar
Now nest by his feet,
Afraid no more.

He turns his face
To the winter moon;
His claws are furled,
His courage gone.

The first owl swoops
To the forest floor;
But the last of the dragons
Is no more.

by Judith Nicholls

What She Did

What she did
was really awful
It made me feel quite ill
It was wrong and quite unlawful
I feel queasy still.

What she did
was quite uncalled for
How could she be so cruel?
My friends were all appalled, for
she made me look a fool.

What she did
was out of order
It made me blush and wince
From that instant I ignored her
and haven't spoken since.

What she did
was really rotten.
But what it was
I've quite forgotten.

by Roger McGough

Zebra Question

I asked the zebra,
Are you black with white stripes?
Or white with black stripes?
And the zebra asked me,
Are you good with bad habits?
Or are you bad with good habits?
Are you noisy with quiet times?
Or are you quiet with noisy times?
Are you happy with some sad days?
Or are you sad with some happy days?
Are you neat with some sloppy ways?
Or are you sloppy with some neat ways?
And on and on and on and on
And on and on he went.
I'll never ask a zebra
About stripes
Again.

by Shel Silverstein

The Clock on the Wall

My city collapsed
The clock was still on the wall
Our neighbourhood collapsed
The clock was still on the wall
The street collapsed
The clock was still on the wall
The square collapsed
The clock was still on the wall
The house collapsed
The clock was still on the wall
The wall collapsed
The clock
Ticked on

by Samih Al-Qasim,
translated by Nazih Kassis from the Arabic

My Dog Smells

My dog smells
The faint scent of
Cats to chase.

Her nose twinkles
Like a black star,
When it's chicken
On Sunday.

She reads the garden
Breeze like a child
With a first comic.
Empty looking air
Is full of information,
Messages incoming as
She fills her lungs.

And when, in the woods,
She finds where
Foxes have been,
She rolls, and then…
… My dog smells!

by Robin Mellor

The Sea

The waves come
tumbling,
rumbling,
crashing,
dashing the harbour wall
and then they fall
back
sighing…
dying…
their strength all gone.
Then another one –
pounding,
sounding like thunder,
surging,
submerging the rocks,
roaring,
pouring into crevices and cracks
with relentless tracks,
beating,
eating the stone!

by Daphne Lister

I Wish

I wish I could have a fish for a pet
now that I've caught one in my net.
But oh, he's wriggly and slippery and wet
I can't have a fish for a pet,
Oh no,
I can't have a fish for a pet.

A crab looks fun with his crusty shell.
He runs so fast on the sand as well.
But his claws look sharp as he moves around
I think he might pinch my feet and my hand.
I can't have a crab for a pet,
Oh no,
I can't have a crab for a pet.

Maybe a whale – he's big as a house.
Although he might frighten my little brown mouse.
His tail would hang over the bath you see,
I can't take a whale home for tea
Oh no,
I can't take a whale home for tea.

I'll have to look at the pets that I've got
My little brown mouse is sweet and furry
My kitten is oh so cuddly and purry
My little black dog has a patch on his nose
And snuggles up on my feet and my toes.
I'll just have to forget the things from the sea
And play with the pets that I've got
You see
And play with the pets that I've got.

by Maureen Phillips

In the Land of Giants

Once everything was big
and you were small,
but year after year your shadow
crept up the wall
and you grew tall.

Quite frightening really
to think of that small shadow disappearing,
to hear that small voice passing out of hearing.

That's the trouble with growing:
you'd like to know where you are going,
but there's no knowing.

by George Szirtes

Level 1 Speaking Verse and Prose

Grade 2 Verse

Vampire

As a vampire, Victor
Was a bit of a dud.
He liked having sharp teeth
But he couldn't stand blood.

"You've got to drink up son,"
Said his father one night.
"You won't grow up strong
If you're frightened to bite."

So out Victor ventured
On the lookout for skin
And found something smooth
To sink his fangs in.

Victor snapped and he snapped
Like a wolf on the loose
And his mouth filled with bits
While his chin ran with juice.

"I've done it dear father,"
Shouted Victor with pride.
"I'm a vampire tonight!
My victim has died."

A vampire he was, but
Not such a scary 'un.
He'd bitten a tomato
So remained, vegetarian.

by Steve Turner

The First Bit

I love the first bit of the morning,
The bit of the day that no one has used yet,
The part that is so clean
You must wipe your feet before you walk out into it.
The bit that smells like rose petals and cut grass
And dampens your clothes with dew.

If you go out you will bump into secrets,
Discover miracles usually covered by bus fumes.
You will hear pure echoes, whispers and scuttling.

I love the first bit of the morning
When the sun has only one eye open
And the day is like a clean shirt,
Uncreased and ready to put on;
The part that gets your attention
By being so quiet.

by Coral Rumble

Be Glad Your Nose Is On Your Face

Be glad your nose is on your face,
not pasted on some other place,
for if it were where it is not,
you might dislike your nose a lot.

Imagine if your precious nose
were sandwiched in between your toes,
that clearly would not be a treat,
for you'd be forced to smell your feet.

Your nose would be a source of dread
were it attached atop your head,
it soon would drive you to despair,
forever tickled by your hair.

Within your ear, your nose would be
an absolute catastrophe,
for when you were obliged to sneeze,
your brain would rattle from the breeze.

Your nose, instead, through thick and thin,
remains between your eyes and chin,
not pasted on some other place –
be glad your nose is on your face!

by Jack Prelutsky

The Sssnake Hotel

An Indian python will welcome you
to the Sssnake hotel.
As he finds you your keys he'll maybe enquire
if you're feeling well.
And he'll say that he hopes
you survive the night,
that you sleep without screaming
and don't die of fright
at the Sssnake hotel.

There's an anaconda that likes to wander
the corridors at night,
and a boa that will lower itself onto guests
as they reach, reach out for the light.
And if, by chance, you lie awake
and nearby something hisses,
I warn you now, you're about to be covered
in tiny vipery kisses,
at the Sssnake hotel, at the Sssnake hotel.

And should you hear a chorus of groans
coming from the room next door,
and the python cracking someone's bones,
don't go out and explore.
Just ignore all the screams
and the strangled yells
when you spend your weekend
at the Sssnake hotel.

by Brian Moses

Mrs Mather

Scared stiff.
Courage flown.
On that doorstep all alone.
Cold sweat.
State of shock.
Lift my trembling hand and knock.

Thumping heart.
Chilled with fear.
I hear the witch's feet draw near.
Rasping bolts.
Rusty locks.
Shake down to my cotton socks.

Hinges creaking.
Waft of mould.
A groan that makes my blood run cold.
Cracking voice.
Knocking knees.
"Can I have my ball back, please?"

by Colin McNaughton

Rain in Summer

How beautiful is the rain!
After the dust and the heat,
In the broad and fiery street,
In the narrow lane,
How beautiful is the rain!

How it clatters along the roofs
Like the tramp of hoofs,
How it gushes and struggles out
From the throat of the overflowing spout!

Across the window-pane
It pours and pours;
And swift and wide,
With a muddy tide,
Like a river down the gutter roars
The rain, the welcome rain!

by Henry Wadsworth Longfellow

Odd Sock Planet

In our house is a drawer
Which is full of odd socks.
They appear from nowhere
And gather in flocks.

I don't know where they come from,
But this I know for sure,
Each time I look inside the drawer
I see a dozen more.

There must surely be a planet
Where odd socks can go and stay
To recover from the trauma
Of sniffing feet all day.

There they walk in perfumed gardens,
And through fields of new mown hay.
For the natives of this planet are
Odd socks that flew away.

So, if you find some of your socks
Have vanished without trace
Just think how happy they must be
Up there, in Outer Space.

by Valerie Waite

Haikus of the Seasons

Summer sun burning
Sunglasses and hot hot skin
– we dream of ice-cream

One red leaf spins down
Where has the year gone already?
The dark comes closer

Hot days in winter
Seasons are falling apart
– pollution warning

Daffodils brighten
We come out into the world
like it's the first time

by John Siddique

Level 1 Speaking Verse and Prose

Grade 2 Prose

Titles in Level 1 Speaking Verse and Prose: Grade 2 Prose

Mr Gum and the Cherry Tree

Down went Polly into the cherry tree. Down she slid through the dark green leaves. Down, down into the very heart of the tree, where the secrets lay. And suddenly she was scared. What if it really *was* Runtus? What if she was about to meet an ancient woodland spirit, a spirit with horns on his head and the legs of a goat and a magic flute so powerful that one note from it could stop the world from turning, or blow up a koala? Shaking like a leaf, Polly pushed aside the shaking leaves. And there she saw him.

Yes, there he was, sitting astride a branch and swigging from a bottle of –

GALLOPING BILL'S HOMEMADE FOREST CIDER

INGREDIENTS:

Cherries, entrails, beer, bit of an old shoe, couple of spiders, somethin' I found in me ear, acorns, magpie beak, fresh lemon juice (not from concentrate)

Counts as two of your recommended five spiders a day

WARNING:

May cause headaches and mild death

It was Mr Gum. His big red scruffler of a beard dripped with cherry juice. His hands were as filthy as pubs. And his bloodshot eyes were lit up with madness and power.

by Andy Stanton

Alana Dancing Star: Samba Spectacular

"Why don't you try out your samba routine?" asked Madame Coco.

"What, right here?" asked Alana shyly.

"Why not?" Madame Coco replied.

"Wait one moment and I do your hair." In seconds, she had scraped back Alana's hair into a high ponytail, and pinned into it a spray of crimson feathers. "Now," she said, "let me see you dance."

Hesitantly, Alana began to do the steps she'd been practising all week. As she danced, she felt a strange tingling sensation on her skin, and her feet felt lighter and began to move faster. Then the ground seemed to disappear underneath her. *What* was going on? Trying not to panic, Alana closed her eyes, but still her feet kept dancing. In the distance, she could still hear Madame Coco's voice. It was saying, "Remember, ma petite, when your good deed is done, the call of home will beckon. You will return home! You will return home!"

The voice faded away and all she could hear was a rushing sound like the wind. Then her feet touched the ground again, but this time it felt warm beneath her. There was hot sunshine, a breeze on her face, and the beat of drums and samba music filling the air.

by Arlene Phillips

Through the Looking-Glass

"It's VERY provoking," Humpty Dumpty said after a long silence, looking away from Alice as he spoke, "to be called an egg – VERY!"

"I said you LOOKED like an egg, Sir," Alice gently explained. "And some eggs are very pretty, you know," she added, hoping to turn her remark into a sort of a compliment.

"Some people," said Humpty Dumpty, looking away from her as usual, "have no more sense than a baby!"

Alice didn't know what to say to this: it wasn't at all like conversation, she thought, as he never said anything to HER; in fact, his last remark was evidently addressed to a tree – so she stood and softly repeated to herself:

> *"Humpty Dumpty sat on a wall:*
> *Humpty Dumpty had a great fall.*
> *All the King's horses and all the King's men*
> *Couldn't put Humpty Dumpty in his place again."*

"That last line is much too long for the poetry," she added, almost out loud, forgetting that Humpty Dumpty would hear her.

"Don't stand there chattering to yourself like that," Humpty Dumpty said, looking at her for the first time, "but tell me your name and your business."

by Lewis Carroll

Tumtum and Nutmeg: A Circus Adventure

The General's whiskers twitched. The bus looked very inviting. He could hear Arthur and Lucy talking on the telephone in the hall. He knew they might come back into the kitchen at any moment, but he was too excited to care.

Then suddenly he felt a cold breeze cutting his ankles; and when he looked round he saw to his surprise that the children had left the garden door open.

He stood there a moment, peering out. The sky had turned black, but he could see the pale outline of the garden path, twisting away in the moonlight.

And suddenly it was as if the moon and the stars were all calling out to him, whispering his name.

With a pounding heart, he pulled open the bus door and clambered into the driver's seat, tossing the whip in beside him. Then he gripped hold of the steering wheel, and flicked on the ignition.

The engine gave a shudder, then a *Vrooom!* and the bus shot forwards across the floor.

"Faster! Faster!" the General cried, slamming his paw on the accelerator. He swerved under the kitchen table, and tore towards the open door.

The spider fled out of his way, and a fly splattered on the windscreen. The General clung tight to his seat as the bus bounced over the doorstep, and crashed on to the garden path. Then, with a shriek of joy, he turned on his headlights, and sped into the night.

by Emily Bearn

Fantastic Mr Fox

While they were talking, the Smallest Fox had sneaked a jar off the shelf and had taken a gulp. "Wow!" he gasped. "Wow-*ee*!"

You must understand this was not the ordinary weak fizzy cider one buys in a store. It was the real stuff, a home-brewed fiery liquor that burned in your throat and boiled in your stomach.

"Ah-h-h-h-h-h!" gasped the Smallest Fox. "This is *some cider*!"

"That's quite enough of that," said Mr Fox, grabbing the jar and putting it to his own lips. He took a tremendous gulp. "It's miraculous!" he whispered, fighting for breath. "It's fabulous! It's beautiful!"

"It's my turn," said Badger, taking the jar and tilting his head well back. The cider gurgled and bubbled down his throat. "It's… it's like melted gold!" he gasped. "Oh, Foxy, it's… like drinking sunbeams and rainbows!"

"You're poaching!" shrieked Rat. "Put that down at once! There'll be none left for me!" Rat was perched upon the highest shelf in the cellar, peering out from behind a huge jar. There was a small rubber tube inserted in the neck of the jar, and Rat was using this tube to suck out the cider.

"You're drunk!" said Mr Fox.

by Roald Dahl

I Don't Believe It, Archie!

"Excuse me!" Archie tapped on the car window. "Is this where the robbery's happening?"

The man in the car looked rather startled. "Robbery?"

"Yes," said Archie. "Is this the right place to come and watch?"

"What…what do you know about a robbery?" asked the man in the car, glancing nervously up and down the street.

"Well, not much," said Archie, "but Cyd's mum has a friend in the police who said they were going to be filming a robbery here today and we thought –"

But Archie never got a chance to say what he thought, because the man in the car suddenly drove off down the road, very fast.

"How rude!" said Archie. "He drove off while I was still talking!"

"I don't believe it!" A big man, dressed all in black, had appeared on the pavement, pulling off a ski mask. He was carrying a baseball bat and a large black bag. "Where's he gone?" he demanded.

"If you're looking for the man in the car," said Archie, "he drove off."

by Andrew Norriss

The Wombles

"Yow!" yelled Orinoco.

The air rushed past him, flattening his fur, and he began to fall faster and faster until there was a whistling sound in his ears.

"Yooow!" roared Orinoco and shut his eyes and the next moment he hit the lake with a tremendous smack, sending up a great shower of water and making every duck swim for cover as hard as it could go. Down and down went Orinoco right to the muddy bottom, and then with his head whirling and his mouth – which had been open at the time – full of weeds he rose slowly to the surface, the umbrella still tightly grasped between his paws.

"I'm coming," panted Bungo, sliding and slipping down the steep bank, and he dived into the Mere for the second time that morning.

Orinoco rolled over on to his back and lay quite still with his eyes closed, his paws crossed over his stomach, the umbrella held between them.

"I've got you," puffed Bungo, fighting his way through the ripples, for Orinoco's fall had set up a widening circle of tidal waves which were now splashing on to the ground. And he put his paws over Orinoco's ears and began to pull him towards dry land, paddling as hard as he could go. Orinoco, as stiff as a poker, was hauled wet and extremely muddy on to the path.

"Are you dead?" Bungo asked anxiously.

"Yes," said Orinoco in a feeble voice, without opening his eyes.

by Elisabeth Beresford

William in Trouble

The curtain rose and the two ladies continued their conversation in a whisper.

"Very pretty," said Mrs Brown.

"Isn't it?" said the other. "Oh, it's quite a nice change to come along to a thing of this sort once in a way."

"Well, I must say," admitted Mrs Brown, "I like to get right away from home sometimes, because really, at home I'm on pins the whole time, not knowing whatever William's going to do next. At a place like this I feel *safe*. It's nice to be anywhere where I *know* that William can't suddenly rise up before my eyes doing something awful."

"Fairy Daffodil!" called the fairy herald on the stage. A figure arose from behind a leafy barrier, took an ungraceful step forward, tripped over the leafy barrier and crashed to earth – leafy barrier and all. The yellow headgear rolled off on to the floor, revealing a tousled head over a stern, earth-streaked freckled face.

"What's your boy like?" said Mrs Brown's neighbour, who was not looking at the stage. "I don't think I've ever seen him."

But Mrs Brown's smile had faded. Her face had become a mask of horror. Her mouth had dropped open. Her neighbour followed her eyes to the stage. The strange apparition was in no wise disconcerted by the strange contretemps with the leafy barrier. It did not even trouble to recover its headgear. It stood in the middle of the stage and said loudly and ferociously "Here I am!"

There was dead silence.

by Richmal Crompton

Level 1 Speaking Verse and Prose

Grade 3 Verse

Aunt Jennifer's Tigers

Aunt Jennifer's tigers prance across a screen,
Bright topaz denizens of a world of green.
They do not fear the men beneath the tree;
They pace in sleek chivalric certainty.

Aunt Jennifer's fingers fluttering through her wool
Find even the ivory needle hard to pull.
The massive weight of Uncle's wedding band
Sits heavily upon Aunt Jennifer's hand.

When Aunt is dead, her terrified hands will lie
Still ringed with ordeals she was mastered by.
The tigers in the panel that she made
Will go on prancing, proud and unafraid.

by Adrienne Rich

Roller Skaters

Flying by
on the winged-wheels
of their heels

Two teenage earthbirds
zig-zagging
down the street

Rising
unfeathered –
in sudden air-leap

Defying law
death and gravity
as they do a wheely

Landing back
in the smooth swoop
of youth

And faces gaping
gawking, impressed
and unimpressed

Only Mother watches – heartbeat in her mouth

by Grace Nichols

The Word Party

Loving words clutch crimson roses,
Rude words sniff and pick their noses,
Sly words come dressed up as foxes,
Short words stand on cardboard boxes,
Common words tell jokes and gabble,
Complicated words play Scrabble,
Swear words stamp around and shout,
Hard words stare each other out,
Foreign words look lost and shrug,
Careless words trip on the rug,
Long words slouch with stooping shoulders,
Code words carry secret folders,
Silly words flick rubber bands,
Hyphenated words hold hands,
Strong words show off, bending metal,
Sweet words call each other 'petal',
Small words yawn and suck their thumbs
Till at last the morning comes.
Kind words give out farewell posies…

Snap! The dictionary closes.

by Richard Edwards

Huff

I am in a tremendous huff –
Really, really bad.
It isn't any ordinary huff –
It's one of the best I've had.

I plan to keep it up for a month
Or maybe for a year
And you needn't think you can make me smile
Or talk to you. No fear.

I can do without you and her and them –
Too late to make amends.
I'll think some deep thoughts on my own for a while,
Then find some better friends.

And they'll be wise and kind and good
And bright enough to see
That they should behave with proper respect
Towards somebody like me.

I do like being in a huff –
Cold fury is so heady.
I've been like this for half an hour
And it's cheered me up already.

Perhaps I'll give them another chance,
Now I'm feeling stronger
But they'd better watch out – my next big huff
Could last much, much, much longer.

by Wendy Cope

The Cats' Protection League

Midnight. A knock at the door.
Open it? Better had.
Three heavy cats, mean and bad.

They offer protection. I ask, "What for?"
The Boss-cat snarls, "You know the score.
Listen man and listen good

If you wanna stay in the neighbourhood,
Pay your dues or the toms will call
And wail each night on the backyard wall.

Mangle the flowers, and as for the lawn
A smelly minefield awaits you at dawn."
These guys meant business without a doubt

Three cans of tuna, I handed them out.
They then disappeared like bats into hell
Those bad, bad cats from the CPL.

by Roger McGough

Small Boy

He picked up a pebble
and threw it into the sea.

And another, and another.
He couldn't stop.

He wasn't trying to fill the sea.
He wasn't trying to empty the beach.

He was just throwing away,
nothing else but.

Like a kitten playing
he was practising for the future

when there'll be so many things
he'll want to throw away

if only his fingers will unclench
and let them go.

by Norman MacCaig

From a Railway Carriage

Faster than fairies, faster than witches,
Bridges and houses, hedges and ditches;
And charging along like troops in a battle
All through the meadows the horses and cattle:
All of the sights of the hill and the plain
Fly as thick as driving rain;
And ever again, in the wink of an eye,
Painted stations whistle by.
Here is a child who clambers and scrambles,
All by himself and gathering brambles;
Here is a tramp who stands and gazes;
And here is the green for stringing the daisies!
Here is a cart runaway in the road
Lumping along with man and load;
And here is a mill, and there is a river:
Each a glimpse and gone forever!

by Robert Louis Stevenson

Refugee

He can't speak a word of English
But the picture he paints needs no words

In it he puts:

guns
bright orange explosions
a house with no roof
children with no shoes
and his mother and father
lying still, as though asleep.
At the bottom he puts himself, tiny and dark,
with a puddle of blue tears at his feet.
Somehow the fat yellow sun at the top of the page
has a smile on its face.

by Lindsay MacRae

Level 1 Speaking Verse and Prose

Grade 3 Prose

Titles in Level 1 Speaking Verse and Prose: Grade 3 Prose

Coraline

Coraline walked down the corridor uneasily. There was something very familiar about it.

The carpet beneath her feet was the same carpet they had in their flat. The wallpaper was the same wallpaper they had. The picture hanging in the hall was the same that they had hanging in their hallway at home.

She knew where she was: she was in her own home. She hadn't left.

She shook her head, confused.

She stared at the picture hanging on the wall: no, it wasn't exactly the same. The picture they had in their own hallway showed a boy in old-fashioned clothes staring at some bubbles. But now the expression on his face was different – he was looking at the bubbles as if he was planning to do something very nasty indeed to them. And there was something peculiar about his eyes.

Coraline stared at his eyes, trying to work out what exactly was different.

She almost had it when somebody said, "Coraline?"

It sounded like her mother. Coraline went into the kitchen, where the voice had come from. A woman stood in the kitchen with her back to Coraline. She looked a little like Coraline's mother. Only…

Only her skin was white as paper.

Only she was taller and thinner.

Only her fingers were too long, and they never stopped moving, and her dark-red fingernails were curved and sharp.

"Coraline?" the woman said. "Is that you?"

And then she turned round. Her eyes were big black buttons.

by Neil Gaiman

Victory

So [her mother] disappears with the pushchair, and Molly looks out at the white dots on the grey water and thinks about England. She feels guilty that her mother is making this transatlantic trip solely on her behalf, but not guilty enough to give it up. The prospect of being in London again has filled her world with hope.

She looks out to sea, beyond the boats. Strictly speaking this is not the sea but Long Island Sound, she knows; Long Island lies somewhere out there, between here and the Atlantic Ocean. But a haze of heat has blurred water and air so that the horizon is lost in a band of grey-white mist, and suddenly from that mist Molly hears a distant boom, like the sound of a massive gun.

She squints into the distance. For a moment she sees through the haze the outline of a great sailing ship, three-masted, square-rigged, with a dim cloud of smoke drifting away from its side. Molly catches her breath; she has never seen anything like it except in pictures.

Then it is gone. Molly strains to see more, but there is only the water and the sky. She feels again an odd sense of being beckoned, as if some soundless voice were calling her. Where has the ship gone?

When they are driving home with a cheerful, victorious Russell, she says to him, "Did you see that tall ship, way out?"

"What ship?" Russell says.

"It was on the horizon. Just like the picture in your room, the Tall Ships Race."

"That was six years ago – none of those ships is around now. *What* did you see?"

Molly looks away, out of the car window. "I expect I was imagining it," she says.

by Susan Cooper

The London Eye Mystery

We took Salim to the Eye because he'd never been up before. A stranger came up to us in the queue, offering us a free ticket. We took it and gave it to Salim. We shouldn't have done this, but we did. He went up on his own at 11.32, 24 May, and was due to come down at 12.02 the same day. He turned and waved to Kat and me as he boarded, but you couldn't see his face, just his shadow. They sealed him in with twenty other people whom we didn't know.

Kat and I tracked Salim's capsule as it made its orbit. When it reached its highest point, we both said, "NOW!" at the same time and Kat laughed and I joined in. That's how we knew we'd been tracking the right one. We saw the people bunch up as the capsule came back down, facing northeast towards the automatic camera for the souvenir photograph. They were just dark bits of jackets, legs, dresses and sleeves.

Then the capsule landed. The doors opened and the passengers came out in twos and threes. They walked off in different directions. Their faces were smiling. Their paths probably never crossed again.

But Salim wasn't among them.

We waited for the next capsule and the next and the one after that. He still didn't appear. Somewhere, somehow, in the thirty minutes of riding the Eye, in his sealed capsule, he had vanished off the face of the earth.

by Siobhan Dowd

The White Giraffe

It was a tunnel, one that smelled strongly of wet rock and animals that dwell in dank, dark places – spiders, baboons and the like. Leopards enjoy those places as well, but Martine consoled herself with the thought that Jemmy would hardly have lived as long as he had if a carnivore resided close by. After one last attempt to talk herself into staying in the lovely valley, she stepped inside.

The tunnel was not much taller than she was and even a small adult would have had to crouch, but gradually it widened and became less claustrophobic. After a while, it turned back on itself. She was beneath the mountain now. From there, the ground rose sharply in a series of steep steps, slick with froggy algae. Martine put the torch between her teeth and scrambled up in an undignified fashion. She made a mental note to smuggle her giraffe-fur, grass and slime-covered jeans into the washing machine before her grandmother noticed them. The vegetable garden excuse was not going to work a second time.

She was halfway up the last step when a hideous screech echoed from the chamber above her. Martine nearly flew over backwards. Her torch flashed around madly as she grabbed a ledge to save herself. Within seconds, the air was filled with a blizzard of flapping wings and high-pitched squeaks. She had unleashed a colony of bats!

by Lauren St John

The Sheep-Pig

Howling in pain, the black dog turned and ran, his tail between his legs. He ran, in fact, for his life, an open-mouthed bristling pig hard on his heels.

The field was clear, and Babe suddenly came back to his senses. He turned and hurried to the fallen ewe, round whom, now that the dogs had gone, the horrified flock was beginning to gather in a rough circle. She lay still now, as Babe stood panting by her side, a draggled side where the worriers had pulled at it, and suddenly he realized. It was Ma!

"Ma!" he cried. "Ma! Are you all right?"

She did not seem too badly hurt. He could not see any gaping wounds, though blood was coming from one ear where the dogs had bitten it.

The old ewe opened an eye. Her voice, when she spoke, was as hoarse as ever, but now not much more than a whisper.

"Hullo, young un," she said.

Babe dropped his head and gently licked the ear to try to stop the bleeding, and some blood stuck to his snout.

"Can you get up?" he asked.

For some time Ma did not answer, and he looked anxiously at her, but the eye that he could see was still open.

"I don't reckon," she said.

"It's all right, Ma," Babe said. "The wolves have gone, far away."

by Dick King-Smith

A Girl Called Dog

Dog's heart raced. She knew these words – knew them in a way she'd never known the words that Uncle spoke. Inside her silent heart, words rose up like a country rising from the sea. The dream-like blur of the huts, the river, the great trees, shimmered into focus, and a memory, a real memory of a time before Uncle, grew inside her like a bright bubble.

She remembered a beach by a river, just like this. She remembered the light on the water, the dry warmth of her mother's arms around her, the safe smell of her mother's skin and the line of blue parrots against the green. Her mother's voice had whispered – whispered words that named the trees, the water, the birds and herself!

The boy stepped out from under the trees into the clearing where the guest hut stood. He had been away from the village for a few days and hadn't seen their visitor. "Hello," he said, a little surprised to find a child rather like himself. "Who are you?"

The answer was in Dog's heart, where her mother had put it. In a voice so tiny it seemed to come from far away, Dog spoke.

"I'm named after the blue macaw," she said. "I'm called Mintak."

by Nicola Davies

How To Be a Pirate

Hiccup forced himself to open his eyes. If he was ever going to be a pirate he would have to get used to this sort of thing. He made himself peer over the edge and into the coffin.

There, in a state of green and yellow decay, lay the corpse of Grimbeard the Ghastly. It wasn't so bad really. The face was all slimy and drippy, but it wasn't crawling with maggots or anything disgusting. Rather peaceful really, lying so still...

And then Hiccup was sure he saw one of the paper-white fingers twitch slightly.

He blinked and stared hard at it.

Nothing for a second.

And then... there it was again, a definite quivering...

"The c-c-corpse!" stuttered Hiccup, "it's m-m-moving!"

"Nonsense, boy!" snapped Gobber the Belch. "How can he possibly move? He's DEAD, isn't he?" And he gave the corpse a prod with one fat forefinger.

The corpse of Grimbeard the Ghastly snapped straight upright, propelled by some appalling force from within it, yellow eyes popping, dribbly green face contorted in a ghastly grimace.

"Aaaaaargh," gurgled the corpse of Grimbeard the Ghastly, straight into the face of Gobber the Belch.

by Cressida Cowell

Born To Run

I'm a running dog, a chasing dog, a racing dog. I'm not a fighting dog. I never in all my life had a fight before that night. My speed had always got me out of trouble before. This time I didn't have a chance to use it. He came at us out of nowhere, leaped straight at my face, teeth bared and snarling. He may have been small but he was all aggression, all muscles, all teeth, and I realised at once that he'd rip my throat out if he could. So I fought back with all my strength because I knew I was fighting for my life. It was him or me.

For a while I gave as good as I got, but I very soon understood that I was neither strong enough nor cunning enough. I was up against a street fighter, a killer dog. As we tussled and tore at each other, I could feel my strength ebbing fast. If Becky had not pulled us apart when she did, it would have ended much worse for me. As it was I got away with a bloodied ear. Becky was not so lucky.

I didn't really know how badly hurt she was until we were through the fence, and running through the streets, until I looked back and saw she was staggering rather than running. I stopped to wait for her. She was leaning against a lamp post now, so I ran back to her. "It keeps bleeding," she said. She was breathing hard and clutching her wrist. "It won't stop bleeding."

by Michael Morpurgo

Level 2 Speaking Verse and Prose

Grade 4 Verse

Hunter Trials

It's awf'lly bad luck on Diana,
    Her ponies have swallowed their bits;
She fished down their throats with a spanner
    And frightened them all into fits.

So now she's attempting to borrow.
    Do lend her some bits, Mummy, *do*;
I'll lend her my own for to-morrow,
    But to-day *I'll* be wanting them too.

Just look at Prunella on Guzzle,
    The wizardest pony on earth;
Why doesn't she slacken his muzzle
    And tighten the breech in his girth?

I say, Mummy, there's Mrs Geyser
    And doesn't she look pretty sick?
I bet it's because Mona Lisa
    Was hit on the hock with a brick.

Miss Blewitt says Monica threw it,
    But Monica says it was Joan,
And Joan's very thick with Miss Blewitt,
    So Monica's sulking alone.

And Margaret failed in her paces,
    Her withers got tied in a noose,
So her coronets caught in the traces
    And now all her fetlocks are loose.

Continued ▸

Oh, it's me now. I'm terribly nervous.
   I wonder if Smudges will shy.
She's practically certain to swerve as
   Her Pelham is over one eye.

Oh wasn't it naughty of Smudges?
   Oh, Mummy, I'm sick with disgust.
She threw me in front of the Judges,
   And my silly old collarbone's bust.

by John Betjeman

Days

Days fly by on holidays,
they escape like birds
released from cages.
What a shame you can't buy
tokens of time, save them up
and lengthen the good days,
or maybe you could tear out time
from days that drag, then pay it back
on holidays, wild days,
days you wish would last forever.
You could wear these days with pride,
fasten them like poppies to your coat,
or keep them in a tin, like sweets,
a confection of days
to be held on the tongue
and tasted, now and then.

by Brian Moses

Everyone Sang

Everyone suddenly burst out singing;
And I was filled with such delight
As prisoned birds must find in freedom,
Winging wildly across the white
Orchards and dark-green fields; on – on – and out of sight.

Everyone's voice was suddenly lifted;
And beauty came like the setting sun:
My heart was shaken with tears; and horror
Drifted away… O, but Everyone
Was a bird; and the song was wordless; the singing will never
   be done.

by Siegfried Sassoon

I Am

I am the person you bullied at school,
I am the person who didn't know how to be cool,
I am the person you alienated,
I am the person you ridiculed and hated.

I am the person who sat on her own,
I am the person who walked home alone,
I am the person you scared every day,
I am the person who had nothing to say.

I am the person with hurt in her eyes,
I am the person you never saw cry,
I am the person living alone with her fears,
I am the person destroyed by her peers.

I am the person who drowned in your scorn,
I am the person who wished she hadn't been born,
I am the person you destroyed for 'fun',
I am the person, but not the only one.

I am the person whose name you don't know,
I am the person who just can't let go,
I am the person who has feelings too,
And I was a person, just like you.

by Laura

Andalucía

Light is a knife flash
over the gilt palace,
breaking wave on the street.
Southern sun in stars
falls through orange groves
in pools on pathways.
Hand-claps, beating hooves.
Black eyes, cutting manes.
Horses dance under palms.
Trailing notes like flight,
guitars sing the sky.
Beyond this, nightfall.
Beyond this, edge of earth.
Memory writes its name on my body.

by Clarissa Aykroyd

Birdfoot's Grampa

The old man
must have stopped our car
two dozen times to climb out
and gather into his hands
the small toads blinded
by our lights and leaping,
live drops of rain.

The rain was falling,
a mist about his white hair
and I kept saying
you can't save them all,
accept it, get back in
we've got places to go.

But, leathery hands full
of wet brown life,
knee deep in the summer
roadside grass,
he just smiled and said
they have places to go to
too.

by Joseph Bruchac

Good Morning, Dear Students

"Good morning, dear students," the principal said.
"Please put down your pencils and go back to bed.
Today we will spend the day playing outside,
then take the whole school on a carnival ride.

"We'll learn to eat candy while watching TV,
then listen to records and swing from a tree.
We'll also be learning to draw on the walls,
to scream in the classrooms and run in the halls.

"So bring in your skateboard, your scooter, your bike.
It's time to be different and do what you like.
The teachers are going to give you a rest.
You don't have to study. There won't be a test.

"And if you'd prefer, for a bit of a change,
feel free to go wild and act really strange.
Go put on a clown suit and dye your hair green,
and copy your face on the Xerox machine.

"Tomorrow it's back to the regular grind.
Today, just go crazy. We really don't mind.
So tear up your homework. We'll give you an A.
Oh wait. I'm just kidding. It's April Fools' Day."

by Kenn Nesbitt

Symphony in Yellow

An omnibus across the bridge
   Crawls like a yellow butterfly,
   And, here and there, a passer-by
Shows like a little restless midge.

Big barges full of yellow hay
   Are moored against the shadowy wharf,
   And, like a yellow silken scarf,
The thick fog hangs along the quay.

The yellow leaves begin to fade
   And flutter from the Temple elms,
   And at my feet the pale green Thames
Lies like a rod of rippled jade.

by Oscar Wilde

Level 2 Speaking Verse and Prose

Grade 4 Prose

Titles in Level 2 Speaking Verse and Prose: Grade 4 Prose

The Roman Mysteries: The Secrets of Vesuvius

Flavia had never been so tired. She tried to concentrate on just placing one foot in front of the other. She prayed to Castor and Pollux, and she prayed to Vulcan – the god of volcanoes – and not for the first time she prayed to the Shepherd. She prayed that she and her friends might live.

Earlier in the evening she had felt hopeful. It seemed as if the volcano was not going to be the disaster they had all feared.

Now she felt only despair. The sun should have risen by now, but it was darker than ever, and all her hope had been quenched by oppressive heat, darkness and exhaustion. She wished she had slept earlier, for now she could barely keep her eyes open.

The refugees had turned on their heels, so that now Gutta and Flavia led the way down along the beach while Pliny and his sailors took up the rear. It seemed as if they had been walking for hours.

There was another awful roar from the mountain behind them and everyone turned wearily to see what new terror the gods had dreamed up.

Although they were miles from Vesuvius, they all clearly saw what happened next.

Of all the horrors the volcano had produced so far, this was the worst.

by Caroline Lawrence

The Wolves of Willoughby Chase

She woke suddenly from one of these dreams to find that the train had stopped with a jerk.

"Oh! What is it? Where are we?" she exclaimed before she could stop herself.

"No need to alarm yourself, miss," said her companion, looking unavailingly out of the black square of window. "Wolves on the line, most likely – they often have trouble of that kind hereabouts."

"Wolves!" Sylvia stared at him in terror.

"They don't often get into the train, though," he added reassuringly. "Two years ago they managed to climb into the guard's van and eat a pig, and once they got the engine-driver – another had to be sent in a relief-engine – but they don't often eat a passenger, I promise you."

As if in contradiction of his words a sad and sinister howling now arose beyond the windows, and Sylvia, pressing her face against the dark pane, saw that they were passing through a thickly wooded region where snow lay deep on the ground. Across this white carpet she could just discern a ragged multitude pouring, out of which arose, from time to time, this terrible cry. She was almost petrified with fear and sat clutching Annabelle in a cold and trembling hand. At length she summoned up strength to whisper:

"Why don't we go on?"

"Oh, I expect there are too many of 'em on the line ahead," the man answered carelessly. "Can't just push through them, you see."

by Joan Aiken

The Sleeping Army

Hypnotised, Freya stood on tiptoe, put her lips around the horn's narrow mouthpiece and blew.

A thunderous roaring ringing shrieking blast rumbled and swelled, pealing and blaring louder and louder and louder until Freya didn't know where her body ended and the sound began.

Freya jerked her mouth away but the ringing horn blasts continued reverberating. The roaring, swelling earthquake exploded around her, clap upon clap of thunder, pealing, clanging, booming, banging, booming, banging, booming, banging until she thought her head would split.

She pressed her hands against her ears but the blasts were inside her now, controlling her heart, her breath, her life's blood.

The white carved ceiling and walls cracked and a gigantic gash zigzagged across the floor. Armour and shields crashed from the walls while all around her was the sickening sound of smashing pottery and glass. Every alarm in the museum went off.

There was a humming in her ears. A feeling as if the moving air was cracking and thinning then thickening around her. There was an overpowering smell of frost and fur. She felt as if her body were breaking apart.

The air hissed and bubbled, splintering into shards of ice. The glass case containing the Lewis Chessmen shattered. Freya was caught up in an icy whirlwind, like a wave snatching her ankles and spinning her through space.

Bob, running into the room shouting her name, glimpsed a queen. A king. A berserk. A riderless horse. And Freya, spiralling together through the air, sucked into a vortex of flashing lights.

Then they vanished.

by Francesca Simon

Little Women

"I don't mean to act any more after this time; I'm getting too old for such things," observed Meg, who was as much a child as ever about 'dressing up' frolics.

"You won't stop, I know, as long as you can trail round in a white gown with your hair down, and wear gold-paper jewellery. You are the best actress we've got, and there'll be an end of everything if you quit the boards," said Jo. "We ought to rehearse to-night; come here, Amy, and do the fainting scene, for you are as stiff as a poker in that."

"I can't help it; I never saw anyone faint, and I don't choose to make myself all black and blue, tumbling flat as you do. If I can go down easily I'll drop; if I can't, I shall fall into a chair and be graceful; I don't care if Hugo does come at me with a pistol," returned Amy, who was not gifted with dramatic power, but was chosen because she was small enough to be borne out shrieking, by the hero of the piece.

"Do it this way; clasp your hand so, and stagger across the room, crying frantically, 'Roderigo, save me! save me!'" And away went Jo, with a melodramatic scream which was truly thrilling.

Amy followed but she poked her hands out stiffly before her, and jerked herself along as if she went by machinery; and her "Ow!" was more suggestive of pins being run into her than of fear and anguish. Jo gave a despairing groan, and Meg laughed outright, while Beth let her bread burn as she watched the fun with interest.

"It's no use! Do the best you can when the time comes, and if the audience shout, don't blame me. Come on, Meg."

Continued ▶

Then things went smoothly, for Don Pedro defied the world in a speech of two pages without a single break; Hagar, the witch, chanted an awful incantation over her kettleful of simmering toads, with weird effect; Roderigo rent his chains asunder manfully, and Hugo died in agonies of remorse and arsenic, with a wild "Ha! Ha!"

"It's the best we've had yet," said Meg, as the dead villain sat up and rubbed his elbows.

by Louisa May Alcott

A Medal For Leroy

I had expected to see simply the back of the photograph, but there was something else there, a writing pad about the same size as the photo. On the front it said, 'Basildon Bond', in fancy printing, and below it, written in pencil, in large capital letters:

'WHO I AM, WHAT I'VE DONE,
AND WHO YOU ARE'
BY
MARTHA MAHONEY
(AUNTIE SNOWDROP)
FOR MICHAEL, SO HE'LL KNOW
FOR HIS EYES ONLY

WRITTEN IN MAY 1950

It took me a little while to cast my mind back, to work it out. This must have been written then about a month or so before she died, because I knew that was in June of 1950. (I checked later in my diary and I was right about that.)

She'd hidden it behind the photo for me to find. Behind the photo! Behind the photo!

Maman called up from downstairs. "*Chéri*, I've got to go down to the shops. Have you got that dog up there? I'd better take him with me. He hasn't had his walk yet. You'll be all right on your own?"

"I'll be fine," I told her. I opened the door to let Jasper out. He didn't seem to want to go even when Maman whistled for him. She had to shout for him more than once. Even then he went only because I pushed him out – I was still cross with him. He gave me a long last look before he left. *Read it*, his eyes were telling me. *Read it*. Then he was gone, scuttling down the stairs. I heard the front door close after them.

Continued ▶

I was alone. I went back to my desk, picked up Auntie Snowdrop's writing pad, sat on my bed, pillows piled behind me, rested the pad on my knees, and opened it. My heart was pounding. I knew even as I began to read – and I have no idea how I knew – that my life would be changed forever, that after I'd read this I would never be the same person again.

by Michael Morpurgo

Half Moon Investigations

It must have been very late, because there wasn't a car on the road. I nipped across and leaned against a gatepost on Rhododendron Road. The fresh air was not perking me up like I thought it would. In fact I felt dizzy and nauseous. No throwing up, I warned myself. Especially not on clients. That would be very unprofessional.

The gate to May's house was open. I crept in, sticking to the grassy verges to avoid crunching the gravel underfoot. Pretty smart thinking for someone suffering the after-effects of anaesthetic.

A fine mist pattered on to my head from the fountain. They must have got it fixed. The water was most refreshing, so I opened my mouth and tried to catch a few drops.

I caught sight of a shadowy figure in an upstairs window. Even in my foggy state it was clear that it was not May or indeed her father, unless one of them had sprouted a beard since we had last met.

I was immediately concerned. Was this my attacker? Had he moved on to his next victim? My heart pumped faster.

Who was this mysterious bearded man and what was he doing in the Devereux house? It was too late to conceal myself in the bushes. I was standing under the moonlight in a pool of white gravel. There was only one approach to take. The direct one.

"Who are you?" I shouted, the words vibrating inside my fragile head. "What are you doing in there?"

The shadowy figure pressed against the glass, beard hair spreading like a halo.

"If you've done anything to May, I will find you."

Continued ▶

The window creaked open and a tremulous voice drifted down to me.

"If you're looking for May Devereux, she lives next door."

I was, of course, outside the wrong house.

by Eoin Colfer

When You Reach Me

Your first note was written in tiny words on a little square of stiff paper that felt like it had once gotten wet. I was packing my knapsack for school when I noticed it sticking out of my library book – which was about a village of squirrels, or maybe it was mice. I had not bothered to read it.

> M,
>
> This is hard. Harder than I expected, even with your help. But I have been practicing, and my preparations go well. I am coming to save your friend's life, and my own.
>
> I ask two favors.
>
> First, you must write me a letter.
>
> Second, please remember to mention the location of your house key.
>
> The trip is a difficult one. I will not be myself when I reach you.

I was freaked. Mom was freaked. She took the morning off and had the locks changed, even though she said that 'M' could be anyone, that this had nothing to do with our missing key, and that the note could have been stuck in that book by anyone, years ago probably, and we'd never know why.

"Isn't it weird, though?" I said. "Our key was just stolen on Friday, and now on Monday we find a note asking where our key is?"

"It *is* weird," Mom said. She put her hands on her hips. "But if you think about it, one thing really can't have anything to do with the other. Someone *with* the key wouldn't have to *ask* where the key is. It makes no sense."

She was right, of course. It was backward. But somewhere in my head a tiny bell started ringing. I didn't even notice it at first.

by Rebecca Stead

Girl, Missing

Annie came inside and shut the door. She ran her fingers over a shelf of little board-books.

"I kept everything just as it was when…" she looked away.

I stood awkwardly, shifting my weight from one leg to the other.

"For years this was the only place I could be still. The only place I could find any peace," Annie said. She walked across the room to where I was standing. Her fingers trembled as she touched my arm. "Would you like to sleep here? We can go through all the baby things another time – decide what you want to keep."

I nodded, then shrank back, pulling my arm away from her hand.

Annie stood there for a few seconds, her hand still outstretched. Then she turned and walked out of the room.

I sank down on the bed. Shelby was right. Annie didn't want me. She wanted the daughter she'd lost. She wanted eleven years of meals and cuddles and plasters on knees.

But she didn't want me. Here. Now. As I was.

And I didn't want her – I wanted the mother I had remembered. The woman I had dreamed.

I curled up into a ball and cried until I fell asleep.

by Sophie McKenzie

Level 2 Speaking Verse and Prose

Grade 5 Verse

Colonel Fazackerley

Colonel Fazackerley Butterworth-Toast
Bought an old castle complete with a ghost,
But someone or other forgot to declare
To Colonel Fazack that the spectre was there.

On the very first evening, while waiting to dine,
The Colonel was taking a fine sherry wine,
When the ghost, with a furious flash and a flare,
Shot out of the chimney and shivered, "Beware!"

Colonel Fazackerley put down his glass
And said, "My dear fellow, that's really first class!
I just can't conceive how you do it at all.
I imagine you're going to a Fancy Dress Ball?"

At this, the dread ghost gave a withering cry.
Said the Colonel (his monocle firm in his eye),
"Now just how you do it I wish I could think.
Do sit down and tell me, and please have a drink."

The ghost in his phosphorous cloak gave a roar
And floated about between ceiling and floor.
He walked through a wall and returned through a pane
And back up the chimney and came down again.

Said the Colonel, "With laughter I'm feeling quite weak!"
(As trickles of merriment ran down his cheek).
"My house-warming party I hope you won't spurn.
You *must* say you'll come and you'll give us a turn!"

Continued ▶

At this, the poor spectre – quite out of his wits –
Proceeded to shake himself almost to bits.
He rattled his chains and he clattered his bones
And he filled the whole castle with mumbles and moans.

But Colonel Fazackerley, just as before,
Was simply delighted and called out, "Encore!"
At which the ghost vanished, his efforts in vain,
And never was seen at the castle again.

"Oh dear, what a pity!" said Colonel Fazack.
"I don't know his name, so I can't call him back."
And then with a smile that was hard to define,
Colonel Fazackerley went in to dine.

by Charles Causley

Extract From a Letter Containing Two Gold Maple Leaves, 1915

… this is a picture, for you,
this is all I can give
from so far away. Unframed:
a clay field
hung with damp November;
spears of wheat piercing the clods
as if the flick of an artist's brush
has spattered with green
the grey;
maple trees still braided with a few leaves
and under my feet the remains of a gold counterpane
on winter's bed;
the field's edge webbed
with tall grasses bending heavy;
the echoing rooks in the big sky;
dewdrops pearled grey and glistening on barbed wire
not far from the front line…

by Judith Green

High Dive

It feels very lonely, up here against the clouds
and girders of the glass roof. The pool so far away,
framed in flowers of a thousand upturned faces.

Walk to the brink, turn, and carefully
(firm toes gripping this last hold on life)
hang heels in space. Face a blank wall.

Raise arms slowly, sideways, shoulder-high,
silent passion, dream-deep concentration
foretelling every second of the coming flight.

Then with a sudden upward beat of palms,
of arms like wings, gathering more than thought
launch backwards into take-off, into one ball

roll for a quadruple reverse somersault
that at the last split second flicks
open like a switchblade –

Feet pointed as in prayer, neat-folded hands
stab the heavens like a dagger, plunge
deep into the pool's azure flesh – without a splash.

by James Kirkup

The Railway Children

When we climbed the slopes of the cutting
We were eye-level with the white cups
Of the telegraph poles and the sizzling wires.

Like lovely freehand they curved for miles
East and miles west beyond us, sagging
Under their burden of swallows.

We were small and thought we knew nothing
Worth knowing. We thought words travelled the wires
In the shiny pouches of raindrops,

Each one seeded full with the light
Of the sky, the gleam of the lines, and ourselves
So infinitesimally scaled

We could stream through the eye of a needle.

by Seamus Heaney

Serious

Awake, alert,
Suddenly serious in love,
You're a surprise.
I've known you long enough –
Now I can hardly meet your eyes.

It's not that I'm
Embarrassed or ashamed.
You've changed the rules
The way I'd hoped they'd change
Before I thought: hopes are for fools.

Let me walk with you.
I've got the newspapers to fetch.
I think you know
I think you have the edge
But I feel cheerful even so.

That's why I laughed.
That's why I went and kicked that stone.
I'm serious!
That's why I cartwheeled home.
This should mean something. Yes, it does.

by James Fenton

The Visitor

A crumbling churchyard, the sea and the moon;
The waves had gouged out grave and bone;
A man was walking, late and alone…

He saw a skeleton on the ground;
A ring on a bony finger he found.

He ran home to his wife and gave her the ring.
"Oh, where did you get it?" He said not a thing.

"It's the loveliest ring in the world," she said,
As it glowed on her finger. They slipped off to bed.

At midnight they woke. In the dark outside,
"Give me my ring!" a chill voice cried.

"What was that, William? What did it say?"
"Don't worry, my dear. It'll soon go away."

"I'm coming!" A skeleton opened the door.
"Give me my ring!" It was crossing the floor.

"What was that, William? What did it say?"
"Don't worry, my dear. It'll soon go away."

"I'm reaching you now! I'm climbing the bed."
The wife pulled the sheet right over her head.

It was torn from her grasp and tossed in the air:
"I'll drag you out of bed by the hair!"

Continued ▶

"What was that, William? What did it say?"
"Throw the ring through the window! THROW IT AWAY!"

She threw it. The skeleton leapt from the sill,
Scooped up the ring and clattered downhill,
Fainter… and fainter… Then all was still.

by Ian Serraillier

Patel's Shop: Indian Bazaar

Inside
the cool dimness
sequined scarves
hang like banners
their fringes moving
on currents of
air and incense;
pot-bellied cushions
like benign satin cats
with many mirror eyes
share shelves with
beaded silken slippers
from the Arabian Nights.

Did Sinbad sail this way?

Outside,
the car park,
tar acrid in the nostrils,
hot metal blinding
eyes narrowed in the sun:

there is only a short step
from one reality to another.

by Hilary Semple

Rose Mining

Gardens are short-lived in the chill
of Flin Flon, Manitoba.

But at dusk each husband comes up
from the ground, with an armful
of roses mined in the chambers
that copper and zinc left behind.

They used to come back blackened,
now they're flushed with rouge
bouquets, dusted with pollen, brush
petals and scents from their clothes.

Peer down this mine and smell
the flowers a quarter mile deep,
a huge rose-bowl that the sun
and the bees know nothing about.

Keep the shaft door closed,
so the buds don't crave the sky
and the gladdened wives
don't bloom before it's evening.

by Clive McWilliam

Level 2 Speaking Verse and Prose

Grade 5 Prose

Macbeth (Shakespeare Stories)

It was night in the castle of Dunsinane, and two figures stood close together in the dark hall. One was a doctor, the other a waiting-woman of the Queen.

"When was it she last walked?" asked the doctor, quietly.

"Since His Majesty went into the field."

"Besides her walking, and other actual performances, what, at any time, have you heard her say?"

"That, sir, which I will not report after her."

"You may, to me…"

"Neither to you nor anyone," said the waiting-woman. "Lo you! Here she comes."

It was the Queen. She carried a taper and was in her night attire. Her eyes were open; but she was asleep.

"What is it she does now?" whispered the doctor. "Look how she rubs her hands."

"It is an accustomed action with her," murmured the woman, "to seem thus washing her hands. I have known her continue in this a quarter of an hour."

"Hark! She speaks," said the doctor eagerly; and he and the waiting-woman listened intently to the strange mutterings of the Queen.

"Out, damned spot! Out, I say!" Her hands seemed to gnaw at each other like feverish mice, and the taper tipped and tilted, making wild shadows behind her. Then she cried out, in a voice that filled the listeners with horror: "Who would have thought the old man to have had so much blood in him?"

Continued ▸

"She has spoke what she should not," whispered the waiting-woman. "I am sure of that."

Then her mistress, the Queen, still rubbing at her hands, complained that the smell of blood would not go; and she who had once told her husband that a little water cleared them of the deed, now cried out in anguish:

"All the perfumes of Arabia will not sweeten this little hand!" Then she drifted away. "To bed, to bed," she sighed. "What's done cannot be undone. To bed, to bed, to bed."

by Leon Garfield

I Shall Wear Midnight

Tiffany liked flying. What she objected to was being in the air, at least at a height greater than her own head. She did it anyway, because it was ridiculous and unbecoming to witchcraft in general to be seen flying so low that her boots scraped the tops off ant hills. People laughed, and sometimes pointed. But now, navigating the stick through the ruined houses and gloomy, bubbling pools, she ached for the open sky. It was a relief when she slid out from behind a stack of broken mirrors to see good clean daylight, despite the fact that she had emerged next to a sign which said: IF YOU ARE CLOSE ENOUGH TO READ THIS SIGN, YOU REALLY, REALLY, SHOULDN'T BE.

That was the last straw. She tipped the stick until it was leaving a groove in the mud behind it, and ascended like a rocket, clinging desperately to the strap, which was creaking, to avoid slipping off. She heard a small voice say, "We are experiencing some turbulence, ye ken. If ye look to the right and tae the left ye will see that there are no emergency exits –"

The speaker was interrupted by another voice, which said, "In point o' fact, Rob, the stick has got emergency exits all round, ye ken."

"Oh aye," said Rob Anybody, "but there is such a thing as style, OK? Just waiting until ye have nearly hit the ground and stepping off makes us look like silly billys."

Tiffany hung on, trying not to listen, and also trying not to kick Feegles, who had no sense of danger, feeling as they always did that they were more dangerous than anything else.

Continued ▶

Finally she had the broomstick flying level and risked a look down. There seemed to be a fight going on outside whatever it was they were going to decide was the new name of the King's Head, but you couldn't see any sign of Mrs Proust. The witch of the city was a woman of resource, wasn't she? Mrs Proust could look after herself.

Mrs Proust *was* looking after herself, by running very fast.

by Terry Pratchett

The Adventure of the Speckled Band (The Adventures of Sherlock Holmes)

How shall I ever forget that dreadful vigil? I could not hear a sound, not even the drawing of a breath, and yet I knew that my companion sat open-eyed, within a few feet of me, in the same state of nervous tension in which I was myself. The shutters cut off the least ray of light, and we waited in absolute darkness.

From outside came the occasional cry of a night-bird, and once at our very window a long drawn catlike whine, which told us that the cheetah was indeed at liberty. Far away we could hear the deep tones of the parish clock, which boomed out every quarter of an hour. How long they seemed, those quarters! Twelve struck, and one and two and three, and still we sat waiting silently for whatever might befall.

Suddenly there was the momentary gleam of a light up in the direction of the ventilator, which vanished immediately, but was succeeded by a strong smell of burning oil and heated metal. Someone in the next room had lit a dark-lantern. I heard a gentle sound of movement, and then all was silent once more, though the smell grew stronger. For half an hour I sat with straining ears. Then suddenly another sound became audible – a very gentle, soothing sound, like that of a small jet of steam escaping continually from a kettle. The instant that we heard it, Holmes sprang from the bed, struck a match, and lashed furiously with his cane at the bell-pull.

"You see it, Watson?" he yelled. "You see it?"

Continued ▶

But I saw nothing. At the moment when Holmes struck the light I heard a low, clear whistle, but the sudden glare flashing into my weary eyes made it impossible for me to tell what it was at which my friend lashed so savagely. I could, however, see that his face was deadly pale and filled with horror and loathing. He had ceased to strike and was gazing up at the ventilator when suddenly there broke from the silence of the night the most horrible cry to which I have ever listened. It swelled up louder and louder, a hoarse yell of pain and fear and anger all mingled in the one dreadful shriek.

by Sir Arthur Conan Doyle

The Wheel of Surya

When Jaspal turned into Whitworth Road, the first thing he saw was the Riley, parked outside Number 18.

Half-collapsing with fright and fatigue and despair, he leaned within the shadows of a side alley. The men from Stepney had come to the house – Mr Elmhirst, Sid and the others. They must have found out that he and his father had escaped from the fire. Now they were waiting for them. Probably they wanted to kill them both, because he and his father knew who had really killed Dave.

Panic flooded his brain, drowning out all clear thoughts, except one – he couldn't go home. He had to stay free. He retreated further down the alley. It ran along the backs of the houses, and he knew that if he followed it, he would come to the bomb site and the security of his own den.

His legs seemed to have lost all their strength and power. He kept stumbling and falling to his knees. As he passed the back of Number 20, a dog began barking furiously. It raced up the fence on the other side from him, snarling into the cracks, as if it smelt his fear and despised him for it.

He reached the bomb site and realised that the heavy smog of the day had suddenly lifted. A moon hung full and free, lighting his way across the rubble. Yet still, in his distress, he wrong-footed, and crashed heavily into a crater full of sharp-edged bricks and broken glass. Clutching a bruised knee, he rolled over on to his back. He stared through streaming eyes, up at a sky as black and vast and star-spangled as an Indian sky. He opened his mouth and gave a long, piercing howl.

"Ma! Oh, Ma! Take me home! Please come and take me home!"

by Jamila Gavin

Pride and Prejudice

Mr Collins made his declaration in form. Having resolved to do it without loss of time, as his leave of absence extended only to the following Saturday, and having no feelings of diffidence to make it distressing to himself even at the moment, he set about it in a very orderly manner, with all the observances, which he supposed a regular part of the business. On finding Mrs Bennet, Elizabeth, and one of the younger girls together, soon after breakfast, he addressed the mother in these words:

"May I hope, madam, for your interest with your fair daughter Elizabeth, when I solicit for the honour of a private audience with her in the course of this morning?"

Before Elizabeth had time for anything but a blush of surprise, Mrs Bennet answered instantly, "Oh dear! – yes – certainly. I am sure Lizzy will be very happy – I am sure she can have no objection. Come, Kitty, I want you up stairs." And, gathering her work together, she was hastening away, when Elizabeth called out:

"Dear madam, do not go. I beg you will not go. Mr Collins must excuse me. He can have nothing to say to me that anybody need not hear. I am going away myself."

"No, no, nonsense, Lizzy. I desire you to stay where you are." And upon Elizabeth's seeming really, with vexed and embarrassed looks, about to escape, she added: "Lizzy, I *insist* upon your staying and hearing Mr Collins."

Elizabeth would not oppose such an injunction – and a moment's consideration making her also sensible that it would be wisest to get it over as soon and as quietly as possible, she sat down again and tried to conceal, by incessant employment the feelings which were divided between distress and diversion. Mrs Bennet and Kitty walked off, and as soon as they were gone, Mr Collins began.

Continued ▶

"Believe me, my dear Miss Elizabeth, that your modesty, so far from doing you any disservice, rather adds to your other perfections. You would have been less amiable in my eyes had there *not* been this little unwillingness; but allow me to assure you, that I have your respected mother's permission for this address. You can hardly doubt the purport of my discourse, however your natural delicacy may lead you to dissemble; my attentions have been too marked to be mistaken. Almost as soon as I entered the house, I singled you out as the companion of my future life."

by Jane Austen

The Vanished

Belief in the haunted gallery was handed down from generation to generation, right up to the day the mine closed, early in the 1990s. Stories persisted of eerie cries for help coming from the tunnel depths, of knocking from behind the rock face, of scrabbling noises as though the trapped miners were trying to claw their way out by their bloody fingernails. Even the rat, the miner's curse and companion, had deserted that section…

"Rats!" Cassie's nose wrinkled. "I hadn't thought about them. Not that I'm bothered," she added quickly, "not that I've seen any about, either. Have you?"

"No. No, I haven't, come to think of it…"

As if on cue, the knocking started. It was different from the faint rapping they had heard before. There were two separate sounds, one ringing and regular as if made by a pick, the other more scraping and clinking, like a shovel.

"What's that?"

Cassie turned. Her ears seemed to move on her head. It felt as though slivers of ice were slipping down the back of her neck. The sound seemed to be coming from behind the smooth wall of the tunnel…

"I don't know…"

Jake went towards the rock face, putting his ear against it. He stepped back, white faced and shaking. There were noises from the other side of the rock. Not human exactly, more like the breathing and groaning of some great creature. Then the sound broke down to gnashing and snarling as of a number of creatures fighting among themselves. The nearest parallel Jake could make was feeding time in the lion enclosure. Whatever was behind there sounded hungry.

Continued ▶

"Come on!" He grabbed Cassie's arm. "Let's get out of here!"

They fled forwards down the tunnel, the light from their helmets veering and weaving, illuminating now the floor, now the ceiling, as the knocking behind them started up again with renewed vigour.

by Celia Rees

Eating Things On Sticks

We knocked on the door. After a moment it opened, and there stood Morning Glory, dressed in some sort of silver tube that barely covered her bottom. Her legs were stuck in furry yeti boots. She wore a lot of bangles on one wrist, and flowers in her hair.

"Tristram!" she cried, and threw her arms around him.

"Hi, Morning Glory!" he said enthusiastically, and patted her silver bottom. "How far's the pub? Poor Harry and I are *starving*."

"I'll fix you something," she offered. "Just let me finish my session first."

"Session?"

"I'm putting myself in harmony with the universe," explained Morning Glory.

Uncle Tristram asked guardedly, "Does it take long?"

"No, no. You go and unpack."

"I think we'll just sit here and wait," said Uncle Tristram. (I think he hoped that we would put her off whatever she was doing enough to hurry things along.) Morning Glory sank cross-legged to the floor and sat there for a minute or two.

"What are you doing?" I asked her.

"Ssh!" she said. "Try not to disturb me. I am sitting quietly in the presence of the apple."

"What apple?"

She pointed. Over in the corner of the room, there was an apple on the floor.

Continued ▶

"I'll bring it closer, shall I?" I offered politely.

"No, thanks," she said. "It's fine just where it is because, right now, I am just being *mindful* of the apple."

"So you don't actually *want* it?"

"No," she said. "Not until it's time to look at it. I'll need it then. And after that, when I'll be *listening* to it."

"Apples don't make a lot of noise," said Uncle Tristram, "unless someone's munching them, of course."

by Anne Fine

Virals

Claybourne Manor is a registered historic landmark, even has its own website. Before departing Morris, I'd combed through online slideshows, trying to get a feel for the layout.

Built just after the Civil War, the house is styled after a nineteenth century Italian manor. Every inch is handcrafted. Crystal chandeliers. Carved wooden mantles. Elaborate moldings. A home fit for royalty. And a Claybourne has always sat on its throne.

I reviewed the stats I'd found on line. Three stories high, the house contains forty rooms, two dozen fireplaces, sixty baths, and a fifty-foot-long entrance hall.

And I planned to pop in and search the place by myself. Tremendous.

A ten-foot wall surrounds the two-acre property. Spikes top it, and ornate iron gates block access to the driveway.

I studied the gates as I walked by. A tourist, intrigued.

Centered in the scrolly wrought iron was the Claybourne family crest, a gray shield with three black foxes surrounded by black and red vines. The family motto arced above the crest: *Virtus vincit invidiam.* Virtue overcometh envy.

Please.

I peered through the bars.

A guard hunched inside a booth beside the drive, attention focused on a small black-and-white TV. Without breaking stride, I continued down the block.

Continued ▶

Twenty yards past the gate, the wall turned a corner and shot back the length of the lot. The next-door neighbors had planted sumac to block their view of the brick. A narrow trail ran between the Claybourne's wall and the shrubs.

I took a deep breath, looked both ways, then scurried down the trail. Fifteen yards from the sidewalk I reached a small service gate.

Right where it's supposed to be.

I dropped to my knees and wiggled the bricks underlying the gate. One felt loose. A sharp tug and it lifted. A key lay in the dirt.

by Kathy Reichs

Level 3 Speaking Verse and Prose

Grade 6 Verse

Titles in Level 3 Speaking Verse and Prose: Grade 6 Verse

The Cheering Rain

Rain comes like a crowd cheering,
hard on tarmac, on canvas.
Everyone cheers with the rain.
A boy runs between stalls to a van

parked in a side street at odd angles.
A man laughs selling baskets of old tomatoes,
Fifty pence because it's Ramadan.
Rain comes loud, dousing

the sultry hours of an August day.
The rain is my unsteadiness,
I could be swept away.
The colours of vegetables flood;

green and scarlet peppers, iridescent
onions, humble brown potatoes.
I scarcely see them, it is simpler
to be with the rain;

the thrill of its sound like a crowd roaring,
like somebody trampling.
We shelter together, you say,
I told you not to come at Ramadan.
I make myself into a desert,

a hard, dry place, safe from the passion
of water and sacrifice.
I cover my hair and listen
to the cheering rain.

by Kate Adams

Flight

Helicopter shudders, lifts off.
We watch its dragonfly shadow
drift like thistledown far below.

Circle the lake, sun splinters
on wooded shoreline and mountains.
Wing towards the lake's head, weave through
rocky defiles to reach hidden
country beyond, wild and remote.
Snow on alpine plateaux lies deep;
beneath, in forested gorges,
silver rivers thread the shadows,
slide towards the lake, where huts cling
to ferny bank and narrow beach:
safe havens for weary trampers.
Mountain peaks rear snowy summits
into the void. Cloud wisps obscure
their dizzy heights, their craggy steeps,
make of this land a mystery,
an unknown, untried wilderness.

Helicopter sinks down, settles
on familiar earth again.
The world's routines envelop us.

by Joan Lees

The Despairing Lover

Distracted with care,
For Phyllis the fair;
Since nothing could move her,
Poor Damon, her lover,
Resolves in despair
No longer to languish,
Nor bear so much anguish;
But, mad with his love,
To a precipice goes;
Where, a leap from above
Would soon finish his woes.
When in rage he came there,
Beholding how steep
The sides did appear,
And the bottom how deep;
His torments projecting,
And sadly reflecting,
That a lover forsaken
A new love may get;
But a neck, when once broken,
Can never be set:
And, that he could die
Whenever he would;
But, that he could live
But as long as he could;
How grievous soever
The torment might grow,
He scorned to endeavour
To finish it so.

Continued ▶

But bold, unconcerned
At the thoughts of the pain,
He calmly returned
To his cottage again.

by William Walsh

Warning

When I am an old woman I shall wear purple
With a red hat which doesn't go, and doesn't suit me,
And I shall spend my pension on brandy and summer gloves
And satin sandals, and say we've no money for butter.
I shall sit down on the pavement when I'm tired
And gobble up samples in shops and press alarm bells
And run my stick along the public railings
And make up for the sobriety of my youth.
I shall go out in my slippers in the rain
And pick the flowers in other people's gardens
And learn to spit.

You can wear terrible shirts and grow more fat
And eat three pounds of sausages at a go
Or only bread and pickle for a week
And hoard pens and pencils and beermats and things in boxes.

But now we must have clothes that keep us dry
And pay our rent and not swear in the street
And set a good example for the children.
We must have friends to dinner and read the papers.

But maybe I ought to practise a little now?
So people who know me are not too shocked and surprised
When suddenly I am old, and start to wear purple.

by Jenny Joseph

Evening: Ponte al Mare, Pisa

The sun is set; the swallows are asleep;
   The bats are flitting fast in the grey air;
The slow soft toads out of damp corners creep,
   And evening's breath, wandering here and there
Over the quivering surface of the stream,
Wakes not one ripple from its summer dream.

There is no dew on the dry grass to-night,
   Nor damp within the shadow of the trees;
The wind is intermitting, dry, and light;
   And in the inconstant motion of the breeze
The dust and straws are driven up and down,
And whirled about the pavement of the town.

Within the surface of the fleeting river
   The wrinkled image of the city lay,
Immovably unquiet, and for ever
   It trembles, but it never fades away...

by Percy Bysshe Shelley

Cats Have No Language

Cats have no language to tell their world.
The moon is a midsummer's madness
That satisfies foolish chroniclers;
But their paws gloat on the captured mouse
(The slither beneath the stair); the silent bat
That drifted on a moonbeam into the house
Slashed a slitted eye into a flicker
And was gone. The moon is too much for the cat.

The light is too much for cats; that is why,
At the human snarl behind the torch
The keen eyes turn slate, a careless slouch
Replaces the studied artistry, frozen flash
Before the kill. They do not like the light
But have no language save the curving slash
And the sideways sculpture at a whisker's touch.
Cats are dumb when they walk in the night.

Cats are clever at night; but the sun
Melts the moon's glitter out of their eyes,
Leaves them children's toys and the green trees.
Now how can fingers soothe the shoulder knots,
Trust the silken purr, the kind eyes? My cat,
I know, I have seen her sleeping thoughts
Tense and stalk savagely in the night's peace.
But cats need no language to do that.

by Vijay Nambisan

At the Border, 1979

"It is your last check-in point in this country!"
We grabbed a drink –
soon everything would taste different.

The land under our feet continued
divided by a thick iron chain.
My sister put her leg across it.

"Look over here," she said to us,
"my right leg is in this country
and my left leg is in the other."
The border guards told her off.

My mother informed me: We are going home.
She said that the roads are much cleaner
the landscape is more beautiful
and people are much kinder.

Dozens of families waited in the rain.
"I can inhale home," somebody said.
Now our mothers were crying. I was five years old
standing by the check-in point
comparing both sides of the border.

The autumn soil continued on the other side
with the same colour, the same texture.
It rained on both sides of the chain.

We waited while our papers were checked,
our faces thoroughly inspected.
Then the chain was removed to let us through.
A man bent down and kissed his muddy homeland.
The same chain of mountains encompasses all of us.

by Choman Hardi

London, 7 July

Ten minutes to nine. Evening
bright and warm from another world but
still it makes me think of you,
light-bound city, whose people that morning
went as always into darkness and for once
didn't emerge. Those names have echoes now
or are echoes, round the streets
so strong they shake loose the knots wound tight
around hearts, freeing tears.

On some other morning at ten to nine
in my greatly enlarged world, you, city,
I will go into that darkness
which is for me freedom, and board a tunnel
of blue light. And whether death comes to me there
or to some other with green eyes
in a city I will never know
it makes no difference. It is not forever,
never has been, nor will ever be.
No illegitimate darkness
is forever. Only that which we love.

by Clarissa Aykroyd

Level 3 Speaking Verse and Prose

Grade 6 Prose

Titles in Level 3 Speaking Verse and Prose: Grade 6 Prose

Refugee Boy

At the meal everyone was cautious. All the members of the family were concerned with Alem's state of mind. Although he was quiet and looked very much in control, none of them knew how much Alem would want to talk about things. Alem was eating very little, very slowly.

"Eat as much as you can, dear," said Mrs Fitzgerald gently.

"Yes, Mrs Fitzgerald," Alem replied.

For a long time the only sound coming from the room was that of the cutlery scraping the porcelain.

"Try and eat some more," Mrs Fitzgerald said. "Eating may not seem that important to you now, and it may not be the best food in the world, but I reckon there's a few of those vitamin and mineral things in there."

"And we all need some of those," Mr Fitzgerald added.

Then it was back to the silence. Another couple of minutes passed and Alem put down his knife and fork as he stared into his food.

Ruth was the first to notice. "What's the matter?" she asked.

Suddenly, Alem burst into tears and began crying loudly. He stamped his feet up and down and began hitting the sides of his clenched fists against his thighs, causing glasses of water to topple on the table. He cried louder, then he put his hands over his ears and shook his head as if he was trying to keep out an evil sound. His sobbing was becoming harder to control; he tried to shout some words in Amharic but that just made him lose control even more. He quickly stood up. The table shook as his thighs hit it, his chair fell to the floor behind him and he ran upstairs.

Continued ▶

They listened to him from downstairs for a while as he cried. He gasped for breath as the crying sapped the energy from him, then they could hear him talking loudly to himself in Amharic, ranting as if he had lost his mind. They couldn't understand what he was saying but somehow it sounded as if he was pleading with someone or begging for something. Slowly, he began to quieten down. They listened as he drew in big, deep breaths; they could hear him trying his best to pull himself together.

by Benjamin Zephaniah

Ithaka

A sound filled Klymene's head like a thousand horses at once drumming their hooves on the earth. She put her hands up to cover her ears and saw the glassy walls of water shifting and moving and swelling and she held her breath as they crashed together and broke in a fountain of foam that seemed almost to touch the dark sky and hang in the air before it fell back to the shore again, and broke on the beach in a line of gigantic waves that roared up as far as the path to the city, and ebbed back and back and broke again, over and over, till Klymene was deafened with the noise of it and shivering with fear.

"The sea is calmer now," said the woman. The owl had settled on her shoulder with its white wings folded. "Antikleia is lost to this world. Go and tell them at the palace, child. Tell them Athene guided her."

"Pallas Athene is a Goddess," said Klymene and the woman smiled.

"Recognize her, then."

Klymene sank to her knees. How could she not have seen? How did she not know at once? Of course – this tall lady with the owl on her shoulder. Of course it was.

"Lady," she breathed, and bent down with her head on the sand, her mind racing, as she wondered what she would tell Ikarios. Would he believe her? Would anyone? When she raised her head, Pallas Athene had disappeared. Klymene looked all around, but the only sign that the Goddess had spoken to her was the sight of the white owl, disappearing towards the horizon. Klymene got to her feet and began to run to the rocks, back to Ikarios, shouting as she went.

"Ikarios! She's dead! Antikleia's gone. She drowned. Ikarios, come, we have to tell them at the palace. Pallas Athene says we have to tell them."

He couldn't hear her, she knew. She was still too far away, but some sound must have reached him because he was looking at her.

by Adèle Geras

The Toymaker

The Toymaker turned and looked at her. "Give the girl a drink, Leiter," he said.

Unhurriedly Leiter filled a small glass from a jug on the table. It took him a moment and he had his back to Katta as he did it. When he turned round, he held the glass out to her. She stared at the glass, then at him.

"It is only water," he said. "Drink it."

She took the glass in both hands, then, like a small child told to take medicine, she put it to her lips and drank, watching Leiter the whole time. Her hands were shaking, but her mouth was so dry. He took the empty glass from her.

"Now, come and see," said the Toymaker.

He was standing beside the young woman, lightly brushing her hair with his hand.

Katta moved closer, and then stopped. Sleeping people breathe; they move – you only have to look carefully enough and you see it. But the young woman on the table wasn't breathing at all. She wasn't dead either – dead people look dead, like Jacob, but she didn't.

Katta looked up at him, not knowing what she was supposed to do.

"Touch her," he said.

Hesitantly she reached out a hand and touched the tips of her fingers against the young woman's cheek. As she did so, Katta's face clouded with confusion and she pulled her hand back, because the skin was hard and cold. She wasn't real at all.

She was a doll.

Continued ▸

"All she needs is a heart, child. When she has a heart, even you would believe that she was real. She will be able to dance and talk, though she will never need to say very many words. Her beauty will speak for her."

Katta looked at the face of the young woman and it seemed to her that she was seeing something she'd seen before – the cold, empty face of the Duke as he had walked beneath her window. She was just like him.

"You see," the Toymaker said, "the people expect their Duke to take a wife."

As he spoke, he picked up from the table a small fine ivory handle. There was nothing else to it that Katta could see.

"All she needs," he said, "is a heart."

by Jeremy de Quidt

Stalking Ivory

The rock slipped in his hand as his own blood flowed from more and more cuts. Jelani wiped them on his torn shirt and took a better grip. He had to escape tonight and soon. His friends were in danger. They might not want him back after what had happened to Biscuit, but he could not let the same thing happen to them.

The leather strap finally yielded to the rock's sharp edge. His hands were free. Now to release his foot from its prison. Jelani took off his torn and bloody shirt and wrapped it around the chain to silence it. Then he pushed against the iron as he pulled his heel back.

The rusty leg iron might have been made for a larger foot, but it still managed to catch his heel. He took his rock tool and sawed away some of the callus on his heel, taking part of the skin with it. Only by lubricating his foot with his own blood and by scraping off the skin of his heel and part of his ankle bone was he able to finally extricate himself. He gathered up his shirt, wrapping it around his sliced palms as a bandage.

Beside him lay the skin of foul water and the handful of dates. He devoured the dates and forced himself to swallow the horrid-tasting water. There was very little of it, and Jelani's thirst made him wish for more no matter how disgusting it tasted.

He dropped the empty skin on the ground next to the ankle iron and slipped out of the camp and back towards the mountain of the elephants. All the while, two words echoed in his head. *Simba Jike.* He needed to warn her.

by Suzanne Arruda

No Great Mischief

Now, in the sky, on the high-rise horizon, seagulls appear caught in the glint of the September sun, and beneath them, but invisible to me, is the white activity of Toronto harbour. Farther south, in the country from which I have come, and to which I will return, the fruit and vegetable pickers bend and stretch wearily. The sweat trickles down the crevices of the weekend pickers and blotches their clothes. The children become grumpy and stage brief sit-down strikes, oblivious to the speeches of their parents who tell them of the money they are saving or of how good the produce will taste in winter. Sometimes the parents criticize them harshly, telling them they are lazy, or uttering speeches, beginning, "When I was a child…" The children look at their hands and are fascinated by the earth beneath their fingernails and mildly fearful of the beginning hangnails and the unfamiliar scratches. "I think I've got a thorn in my finger," they say. "What time is it now?" "Haven't we got enough?" "If I promise not to eat any of this stuff in the winter can I stop picking now?" "My thumb is bleeding. I can see my own blood." "I wish I had something to drink."

In other fields the imported pickers move with quiet speed. Sometimes they look towards the sun to gauge the time, and sometimes they stand straight and place their hands to the smalls of their backs but never for long. Their eyes scan the rows and the branches and the full and the empty baskets. They are counting all the time and doing primitive arithmetic within their heads. They do not sweat, and their children do not complain. When the sun goes down, this Saturday evening, the field owner may sell them cases of beer purchased from the local beer store or some of the men may find their way to certain taverns. The strictly religious and the most fearful will not go. Those who do go sit by themselves and talk in their own languages and some add up present and future totals on

Continued ▶

cigarette packages. Many of them are imagining themselves back home, as they sit nervously tearing the beer labels off their bottles or drumming their blunt brown fingers on the uneven surfaces of the crowded tables, slopped with beer.

I do not know what to buy for my brother or for myself. What to buy for the men who have everything or nothing.

"It doesn't make much difference," he said. "It doesn't make much difference." Pick your own.

by Alistair MacLeod

The Hunger Games

Cinna jumps off the chariot and has one last idea. He shouts something up at us, but the music drowns him out. He shouts again and gestures.

"What's he saying?" I ask Peeta. For the first time, I look at him and realize that ablaze with the fake flames, he is dazzling. And I must be, too.

"I think he said for us to hold hands," says Peeta. He grabs my right hand in his left, and we look to Cinna for confirmation. He nods and gives a thumbs up, and that's the last thing I see before we enter the city.

The crowd's initial alarm at our appearance quickly changes to cheers and shouts of "District Twelve!" Every head is turned our way, pulling the focus from the three chariots ahead of us. At first, I'm frozen, but then I catch sight of us on a large television screen and am floored by how breathtaking we look. In the deepening twilight, the firelight illuminates our faces. We seem to be leaving a trail of fire off the flowing capes. Cinna was right about the minimal make-up; we both look more attractive but utterly recognizable.

Remember, heads high. Smiles. They're going to love you! I hear Cinna's voice in my head. I lift my chin a bit higher, put on my most winning smile, and wave with my free hand. I'm glad now I have Peeta to clutch for balance; he is so steady, solid as a rock. As I gain confidence, I actually blow a few kisses to the crowd. The people of the Capitol are going nuts, showering us with flowers, shouting our names, our first names, which they have bothered to find on the programme.

The pounding music, the cheers, the admiration work their way into my blood, and I can't suppress my excitement. Cinna has given me a great advantage. No one will forget me. Not my look, not my name. Katniss. The girl who was on fire.

by Suzanne Collins

The Thirty-Nine Steps

I heard a noise in the sky, and lo and behold there was that infernal aeroplane, flying low, about a dozen miles to the south and rapidly coming towards me.

I had the sense to remember that on a bare moor I was at the aeroplane's mercy, and that my only chance was to get to the leafy cover of the valley. Down the hill I went like blue lightning, screwing my head round, whenever I dared, to watch that damned flying machine. Soon I was on a road between hedges, and dipping to the deep-cut glen of a stream. Then came a bit of thick wood where I slackened speed.

Suddenly on my left I heard the hoot of another car, and realised to my horror that I was almost up on a couple of gateposts through which a private road debouched on the highway. My horn gave an agonised roar, but it was too late. I clapped on my brakes, but my impetus was too great, and there before me a car was sliding athwart my course. In a second there would have been the deuce of a wreck. I did the only thing possible, and ran slap into the hedge on the right, trusting to find something soft beyond.

But there I was mistaken. My car slithered through the hedge like butter, and then gave a sickening plunge forward. I saw what was coming, leapt on the seat and would have jumped out. But a branch of hawthorn got me in the chest, lifted me up and held me, while a ton or two of expensive metal slipped below me, bucked and pitched, and then dropped with an almighty smash fifty feet to the bed of the stream.

by John Buchan

Nicholas Nickleby

"Does no other profession occur to you, which a young man of your figure and address could take up easily, and see the world to advantage in?" asked the manager.

"No," said Nicholas, shaking his head.

"Why, then, I'll tell you one," said Mr Crummles, throwing his pipe into the fire, and raising his voice. "The stage."

"The stage!" cried Nicholas, in a voice almost as loud.

"The theatrical profession," said Mr Vincent Crummles. "I am in the theatrical profession myself, my wife is in the theatrical profession, my children are in the theatrical profession. I had a dog that lived and died in it from a puppy; and my chaise-pony goes on, in Timour the Tartar. I'll bring you out, and your friend too. Say the word. I want a novelty."

"I don't know anything about it," rejoined Nicholas, whose breath had been almost taken away by this sudden proposal. "I never acted a part in my life, except at school."

"There's genteel comedy in your walk and manner, juvenile tragedy in your eye, and touch-and-go farce in your laugh," said Mr Vincent Crummles. "You'll do as well as if you had thought of nothing else but the lamps, from your birth downwards."

Nicholas thought of the small amount of small change that would remain in his pocket after paying the tavern bill; and he hesitated.

"You can be useful to us in a hundred ways," said Mr Crummles. "Think what capital bills a man of your education could write for the shop-windows."

Continued ▶

"Well, I think I could manage that department," said Nicholas.

"To be sure you could," replied Mr Crummles. "'For further particulars see small hand-bills' – we might have half a volume in every one of 'em. Pieces too; why, you could write us a piece to bring out the whole strength of the company, whenever we wanted one."

"I am not quite so confident about that," replied Nicholas. "But I dare say I could scribble something now and then, that would suit you."

by Charles Dickens

Level 3 Speaking Verse and Prose

Grade 7 Verse

Titles in Level 3 Speaking Verse and Prose: Grade 7 Verse

Backstage

All words by heart as I stand in the dark,
I blank them and breathe, breathe,
they will not leave me.
I am my father's good daughter.
I am my lord's true lover.
I am my own twin brother.
All moves off pat as I wait behind curtains.

All scenes rehearsed as I pause here, certain,
bend at the neck, waist, knees, listen out
for my cue line, inhale, exhale.
I will lose my reason.
I will swallow the poison.
All lines on the tip of my tongue in this dusty gloom.

All text committed as I walked from the green room.
A dead man wrote it.
I have the living throat for a poem.
I have the seeing eyes for a dream.
All dialogue learned as I bide in the wings.

All speeches sure, all lyrics to sing
pitched and prepared, all business timed.
I am the reason and rhyme.
All verbals sorted as I near the stage.

Continued ▶

All ad libs inked on the prompter's page.
I will not corpse.
All black as I prowl at the edge of the limelight.

All rewrites scanned as I squint at the spotlight.
I am Queen of Egypt.

All hushed backstage as I pray the script.

by Carol Ann Duffy

Death Rains

Fields green,
Maize stalks swaying,
Spiking upwards.
Swelling cobs promise
Satisfaction, lives well lived.

Cool rain soaks down
Runs in streams,
Awakening rivers.
Laughter rings as
Children's play shapes
Dams and roads.

We never listen to the thunder;
Lightning's strike is far away –
A distant victim.

Wind's moan begins,
Its rising voice,
Ascending shrieks
Pierce darkened sky.
Towering nimbus
Open on us –
Spill blood-rain.

No god's hand this
But human devilry
Shredding stalks,
Crushing cobs
Child cut from mother, father felled,
Goats and chickens drowned in torrents

Continued ▶

Emptying stomachs,
Crumbling huts, poisoning wells
Flattening hope.

Stealing the promise, the present, the future…

I never told you how I felt
Because I couldn't.
No words,
No tears

by Mary Ndlovu

from **The Prologue to the Canterbury Tales**

A worthy *woman* from beside *Bath* city
Was with us, somewhat deaf, which was a pity.
In making cloth she showed so great a bent
She bettered those of Ypres and of Ghent.
In all the parish not a dame dared stir
Towards the altar steps in front of her,
And if indeed they did, so wrath was she
As to be quite put out of charity.
Her kerchiefs were of finely woven ground;
I dared have sworn they weighed a good ten pound,
The ones she wore on Sunday, on her head.
Her hose were of the finest scarlet red
And gartered tight; her shoes were soft and new.
Bold was her face, handsome, and red in hue.
A worthy woman all her life, what's more
She'd had five husbands, all at the church door,
Apart from other company in youth;
No need just now to speak of that, forsooth.
And she had thrice been to Jerusalem,
Seen many strange rivers and passed over them;
She'd been to Rome and also to Boulogne,
St James of Compostella and Cologne,
And she was skilled in wandering by the way.
She had gap-teeth, set widely, truth to say.
Easily on an ambling horse she sat
Well wimpled up, and on her head a hat
As broad as is a buckler or a shield;
She had a flowing mantle that concealed

Continued ▶

Large hips, her heels spurred sharply under that.
In company she liked to laugh and chat
And knew the remedies for love's mischances,
An art in which she knew the oldest dances.

by Geoffrey Chaucer,
translated by Nevill Coghill from the Middle English

Macavity: The Mystery Cat

Macavity's a Mystery Cat: he's called the Hidden Paw –
For he's the master criminal who can defy the Law.
He's the bafflement of Scotland Yard, the Flying Squad's despair:
For when they reach the scene of crime – *Macavity's not there*!

Macavity, Macavity, there's no one like Macavity,
He's broken every human law, he breaks the law of gravity.
His powers of levitation would make a fakir stare,
And when you reach the scene of crime – *Macavity's not there*!
You may seek him in the basement, you may look up in the air –
But I tell you once and once again, *Macavity's not there*!

Macavity's a ginger cat, he's very tall and thin;
You would know him if you saw him, for his eyes are sunken in.
His brow is deeply lined with thought, his head is highly domed;
His coat is dusty from neglect, his whiskers are uncombed.
He sways his head from side to side, with movements like a snake;
And when you think he's half asleep, he's always wide awake.

Macavity, Macavity, there's no one like Macavity,
For he's a fiend in feline shape, a monster of depravity.
You may meet him in a by-street, you may see him in the square –
But when a crime's discovered, then *Macavity's not there*!

He's outwardly respectable. (They say he cheats at cards.)
And his footprints are not found in any file of Scotland Yard's.
And when the larder's looted, or the jewel-case is rifled,
Or when the milk is missing, or another Peke's been stifled,
Or the greenhouse glass is broken, and the trellis past repair –
Ay, there's the wonder of the thing! *Macavity's not there*!

Continued ▶

And when the Foreign Office finds a Treaty's gone astray,
Or the Admiralty lose some plans and drawings by the way,
There may be a scrap of paper in the hall or on the stair –
But it's useless to investigate – *Macavity's not there*!
And when the loss has been disclosed, the Secret Service say:
"It *must* have been Macavity!" – but he's a mile away.
You'll be sure to find him resting, or a-licking of his thumbs,
Or engaged in doing complicated long division sums.

Macavity, Macavity, there's no one like Macavity,
There never was a Cat of such deceitfulness and suavity.
He always has an alibi, and one or two to spare:
At whatever time the deed took place – MACAVITY WASN'T
   THERE!
And they say that all the Cats whose wicked deeds are widely known
(I might mention Mungojerrie, I might mention Griddlebone)
Are nothing more than agents for the Cat who all the time
Just controls their operations: the Napoleon of Crime!

by T S Eliot

Rubaiyat

for Telajune

Beyond the view of crossroads ringed with breath
her bed appears, the old-rose covers death
has smoothed and stilled; her fingers lie inert,
her nail-file lies beside her in its sheath.

The morning's work over, her final chore
was 'breaking up the sugar' just before
siesta, sitting crosslegged on the carpet,
her slippers lying neatly by the door.

The image of her room behind the pane,
though lost as the winding road shifts its plane,
returns on every straight, like signatures
we trace on glass, forget and find again.

I have inherited her tools: her anvil,
her axe, her old scrolled mat, but not her skill;
and who would choose to chip at sugar-blocks
when sugar-cubes are boxed beside the till?

The scent of lilacs from the road reminds me
of my own garden: a neighbouring tree
grows near the fence. At night its clusters loom
like lantern-moons, pearly-white, unearthly.

I don't mind that the lilac's roots aren't mine.
Its boughs are, and its blooms. It curves its spine
towards my soil and litters it with dying
stars: deadheads I gather up like jasmine.

Continued ▸

My grandmother would rise and take my arm,
then sifting through the petals in her palm
would place in mine the whitest of them all:
"Salaam, dokhtare-mahe-man, salaam!"

"Salaam, my daughter-lovely-as-the-moon!"
Would that the world could see me, Telajune,
through your eyes! Or that I could see a world
that takes such care to tend what fades so soon.

by Mimi Khalvati

The Mayo Tao

I have abandoned the dream kitchens for a low fire
and a prescriptive literature of the spirit;
a storm snores on the desolate sea.
The nearest shop is four miles away –
when I walk there through the shambles
of the morning for tea and firelighters
the mountain paces me in a snow-lit silence.
My days are spent in conversation
with deer and blackbirds;
at night fox and badger gather at my door.
I have stood for hours
watching a salmon doze in the tea-gold dark,
for months listening to the sob story
of a stone in the road, the best,
most monotonous sob story I have ever heard.

I am an expert on frost crystals
and the silence of crickets, a confidant
of the stinking shore, the stars in the mud –
there is an immanence in these things
which drives me, despite my scepticism,
almost to the point of speech,
like sunlight cleaving the lake mist at morning
or when tepid water
runs cold at last from the tap.

I have been working for years
on a four-line poem
about the life of a leaf;
I think it might come out right this winter.

by Derek Mahon

Breakfast

He put the coffee
In the cup
He put the milk
In the cup of coffee
He put the sugar
In the *café au lait*
With the coffee spoon
He stirred
He drank the *café au lait*
And he set down the cup
Without a word to me
He lit
A cigarette
He made smoke-rings
With the smoke
He put the ashes
In the ash-tray
Without a word to me
Without a look at me
He got up
He put
His hat upon his head
He put his raincoat on
Because it was raining
And he left
In the rain
Without a word
Without a look at me
And I   I took
My head in my hand
And I cried.

by Jacques Prévert,
translated by Lawrence Ferlinghetti from the French

Jamaican Bus Ride

The live fowl squatting on the grapefruit and bananas
in the basket of the copper-coloured lady
is gloomy but resigned.
The four very large baskets on the floor
are in everybody's way,
as the conductor points out
loudly, often, but in vain.

Two quadroon dandies are disputing
who is standing on whose feet.

When we stop,
a boy vanishes through the door marked ENTRANCE;
but those entering through the door marked EXIT
are greatly hindered by the fact that when we started
there were twenty standing,
and another ten have somehow inserted themselves
into invisible crannies
between dark sweating body and body.

With an odour of petrol
both excessive and alarming
we hurtle hell-for-leather
between crimson bougainvillaea blossom
and scarlet poinsettia
and miraculously do not run over
three goats, seven hens and a donkey
as we pray
that the driver has not fortified himself
at Daisy's Drinking Saloon
with more than four rums:
or by the gods of Jamaica
this day is our last!

by A S J Tessimond

Level 3 Speaking Verse and Prose

Grade 7 Prose

Brave New World

Three men with spraying machines buckled to their shoulders pumped thick clouds of *soma* vapour into the air. Two more were busy round the portable Synthetic Music Box. Carrying water pistols charged with a powerful anaesthetic, four others had pushed their way into the crowd and were methodically laying out, squirt by squirt, the more ferocious of the fighters.

"Quick, quick!" yelled Bernard. "They'll be killed if you don't hurry. They'll... Oh!" Annoyed by his chatter, one of the policemen had given him a shot from his water pistol. Bernard stood for a second or two wambling unsteadily on his legs that seemed to have lost their bones, their tendons, their muscles, to have become mere sticks of jelly, and at last not even jelly – water: he tumbled in a heap on the floor.

Suddenly, from out of the Synthetic Music Box a voice began to speak. The Voice of Reason, the Voice of Good Feeling. The sound-track roll was unwinding itself in Synthetic Anti-Riot Speech Number Two (Medium Strength). Straight from the depths of a non-existent heart, "My friends, my friends!" said the Voice so pathetically, with a note of such infinitely tender reproach that, behind their gas-masks, even the policemen's eyes were momentarily dimmed with tears, "what is the meaning of this? Why aren't you all being happy and good together? Happy and good," the Voice repeated. "At peace, at peace." It trembled, sank into a whisper and momentarily expired. "Oh, I do want you to be happy," it began, with a yearning earnestness. "I do so want you to be good! Please, please be good and..."

Continued ▶

Two minutes later the Voice and the *soma* vapour had produced their effect. In tears, the Deltas were kissing and hugging one another – half a dozen twins at a time in a comprehensive embrace. Even Helmholtz and the Savage were almost crying. A fresh supply of pill-boxes was brought in from the Bursary; a new distribution was hastily made and, to the sound of the Voice's richly affectionate, baritone valedictions, the twins dispersed, blubbering as though their hearts would break. "Good-bye, my dearest, dearest friends, Ford keep you! Good-bye, my dearest, dearest friends, Ford keep you. Good-bye, my dearest, dearest…"

When the last of the Deltas had gone the policeman switched off the current. The angelic Voice fell silent.

by Aldous Huxley

The Shadow of the Sun

The sun was climbing higher and higher. The desert, that motionless, petrified ocean, absorbed its rays, grew hotter, and began to burn. The hour was approaching when everything would become a hell – the earth, the sky, us. The Yoruba are said to believe that if a man's shadow abandons him, he will die. All the shadows were beginning to shrink, dwindle, fade. The dread afternoon hours were almost upon us, the time of day when people and objects have no shade, exist and yet do not exist, reduced to a glowing, incandescent whiteness.

I thought that this moment had arrived, but suddenly I noticed before me an utterly different sight. The lifeless, still horizon – so crushed by the heat that it seemed nothing could ever issue forth from it – all at once sprang to life and became green. As far as the eye could see stood tall, magnificent palm trees, entire groves of them along the horizon, growing thickly, without interruption. I also saw lakes – yes, enormous blue lakes, with animated, undulating surfaces. Gorgeous shrubs also grew there, with wide-spreading branches of a fresh, intense, succulent, deep green. All this shimmered continuously, sparkled, pulsated, as if it were wreathed in a light mist, soft-edged and elusive. And everywhere – here, around us, and there, on the horizon – a profound, absolute silence reigned: the wind did not blow, and the palm groves had no birds.

"Salim!" I called. "Salim!"

A head emerged from under the hood. He looked at me.

"Salim!" I repeated once more, and pointed.

Continued ▸

Salim glanced where I had shown him, unimpressed. In my dirty, sweaty face he must have read wonder, bewilderment, and rapture – but also something else besides, which clearly alarmed him, for he walked up to the side of the truck, untied one of the goatskins, took a few sips, and wordlessly handed me the rest. I grabbed the rough leather sack and began to drink. Suddenly dizzy, I leaned my shoulder against the truck bed so as not to fall. I drank and drank, sucking fiercely on the goat's leg and still staring at the horizon. But as I felt my thirst subsiding, and the madness within me dying down, the green vista began to vanish. Its colors faded and paled, its contours shrank and blurred. By the time I had emptied the goatskin, the horizon was once again flat, empty and lifeless.

by Ryszard Kapuściński,
translated by Klara Glowczewska from the Polish

The Double Comfort Safari Club

Later that night, much later, Mma Ramotswe awoke. At first she had no idea why – perhaps it was a bad dream – but she suddenly found herself wide awake. The curtain across the window made the room pitch dark, and it was silent too, with only the faint sound of Mma Makutsi's breathing on the other side. Then she heard the sound. It must have penetrated the veils of sleep and prodded her into consciousness. There it was – a curious sniffing sound.

Her thoughts went immediately to snakes. There was a particular sort of snake, the puff adder, that made a sound like that when it was agitated. Those snakes were always finding their way inside and causing terrible trouble. Perhaps there was one in the room already, sliding its way across the floor to where she lay. She sat bolt upright. The sound came again, and this time she was able to locate it as being outside the room. It was definitely outside, and she had decided now that this was no snake.

She rose to her feet and crept silently across the room to the low window. Very slowly, she drew the curtain and peered outside. The moon was a sliver away from fullness, bathing the staff quarters and the surrounding bush in silver light. Her eyes took a moment to adjust, and then everything was clear, sharply delineated enough to throw ghostly moon shadows on the ground.

She looked, and saw, barely an arm's length away from the gauze window, looking directly in at her, a fully grown lion. He looked straight at her, surprised, and she saw for a moment the moon in his eyes. Then, with a sudden tensing of muscle and a whipping movement of his tail, he turned and shot back into the bush. It happened so quickly that she wondered for a moment whether she had imagined it, but there was a rustle of leaves in the bush where he had run, and that was proof that this was no dream, no illusion.

Continued ▸

She heard her heart thumping within her, her mouth dry from shock and fear. She stared at the place where only seconds ago the lion had been; she would not have been surprised had she seen his shadow in the moonlight, imprinted on the ground, as a shadow will register on a photographic plate, caught, as now, in silver.

by Alexander McCall Smith

Trespass

Fire came to the hills behind La Callune.

A thoughtless rambler discards a cigarette.

A dry leaf begins to burn…

The mistral chivvied the flames across the skyline. The wind blew from the north and the fire, gorged by pine resin on the high tops, paused for a moment, then changed direction and began an assault on the valley.

The air was filled with smoke and with the wailing of the fire trucks. Marianne Viala came panting up the road to Audrun's bungalow and the two elderly women stood by the gate, watching. They'd watched it before, year upon year: Cévenol fire in all its heartless grandeur. They'd seen the sky turn black. They'd seen the vinefields greyed and choked with ash. They'd seen power lines explode. But never before had they seen it come straight towards them like this, straight towards the Mas Lunel on the veering wind.

Marianne clutched Audrun's hand. The fire-fighters struggled up the steep terraces with their heavy hoses.

"The *canadairs* are on their way," said Marianne. "Luc called Jeanne and she rang me. The *canadairs* will put it out, Audrun. They're at the coast now, refuelling with water."

Audrun stared up. What fascinated her about fire was the way it appeared so alive. In its crackling and spitting, she could almost hear its boast: *The earth is mine, the tinder-dry earth has always been mine.*

Continued ▶

In contrast to the tireless, boastful fire, Audrun felt like a shadow. She knew she was faltering on the edge of one of her *episodes*. She knew she ought to go and lie down, now, before it began. But she was trying to fight it off this time. She clung to Marianne, with her head lowered, her vision concentrated on the ground at her feet. Sometimes, it could be fought like this, with her concentration on the earth, with her will alone.

When she next looked up, Raoul Molezon was there, his pickup on the driveway. She heard Marianne say to him: "She's not well, Raoul. She's going to go…"

But there was no time to think about this. Audrun herself knew that there was no time. She felt the touch of Raoul's hand on her arm. "The dogs," he almost shouted at her. "I'm going to set the dogs free."

"The dogs?"

"You can't let the dogs be burned alive!"

by Rose Tremain

Dot Robot: Cyber Gold

Master Kojima's words were snatched away by the sound of locks sliding open on a door at the end of the tunnel. The door opened and the figure of a guard with an automatic rifle hanging from his shoulders appeared in the doorway, motioning to the boy holding Master Kojima to come forward.

"Bring him!" the boy commanded two gang members who had watched the interrogation from the shadows. Then he dropped his grip on Master Kojima and walked towards the open doorway, while the two boys took an arm each and dragged Master Kojima after him.

It was dark outside, but as Master Kojima was brought out to an open area surrounded by the concrete perimeter wall, he was blinded by the harsh white light from two powerful headlamps. He instantly knew the source of the intense light and he was terrified.

The fingers of his damaged hand throbbed as he raised an elbow to block the light. What he saw was the outline of a Mech, a five-metre high bi-pedal robotic suit that approximated the shape of a human but was at least twice as high as the tallest person he'd ever seen. The machine had two huge metal arms with large metal pincers for hands, both of which were raised high in front of the steel alloy cage, which served as the cockpit in which the scary-looking robot's guard operator sat. Master Kojima had seen the Mechs at work in the forest in the first few days at the camp. They were used as human-assisted lumberjack robots, which carried and stacked logs and helped with the construction of the wooden parts of the fortress where the children were held.

Continued ▶

From what Master Kojima could see in the dazzling light, the Mech towering above him was holding something between its hydraulic pincers – and it wasn't a log.

The earth between Master Kojima trembled as the Mech took two steps forward. Then its huge pincers opened, and the object it was holding fell to the ground.

Master Kojima looked in horror. Lying in front of him was the motionless body of his sister.

by Jason Bradbury

Jamaica Inn

The light of her candle played upon the walls, but it did not reach to the top of the stairs, where the darkness gaped at her like a gulf.

She knew she could never climb those stairs again, nor tread that empty landing. Whatever lay beyond her and above must rest there undisturbed. Death had come upon the house to-night, and its brooding spirit still hovered in the air. She felt now that this was what Jamaica Inn had always waited for and feared. The damp walls, the creaking boards, the whispers in the air, and the footsteps that had no name: these were the warning of a house that had felt itself long threatened.

Mary shivered; and she knew that the quality of this silence had origin in far-off buried and forgotten things.

She dreaded panic, above all things; the scream that forced itself to the lips, the wild stumble of groping feet and hands that beat the air for passage. She was afraid that it might come to her, destroying reason; and, now that the first shock of discovery had lessened, she knew that it might force its way upon her, close in and stifle her. Her fingers might lose their sense of grip and touch, and the candle fall from her hands. Then she would be alone, and covered by the darkness. The tearing desire to run seized hold of her, and she conquered it. She backed away from the hall towards the passage, the candle flickering in the draught of air, and when she came to the kitchen and saw the door still open to the patch of garden, her calm deserted her, and she ran blindly through the door to the cold free air outside, a sob in her throat, her outstretched hands grazing the stone wall as she turned the corner of the house. She ran like a thing pursued across the yard, and came to the open road, where the familiar stalwart figure of the squire's groom confronted her. He put out his hands to save her, and she groped at his belt, feeling for security, her teeth chattering now in the full shock of reaction.

Continued ▶

"He's dead," she said; "he's dead there on the floor. I saw him"; and, try as she did, she could not stop this chattering of her teeth and the shivering of her body. He led her to the side of the road, back to the trap, and he reached for the cloak and put it around her, and she held it to her close, grateful for the warmth.

"He's dead," she repeated; "stabbed in the back; I saw the place where his coat was rent, and there was blood. He lay on his face. The clock had fallen with him. The blood was dry; and he looked as though he had lain there for some time. The inn was dark and silent. No one else was there."

by Daphne Du Maurier

Down Under

I am not, I regret to say, a discreet and fetching sleeper. Most people when they nod off look as they could do with a blanket; I look as if I could do with medical attention. I sleep as if injected with a powerful experimental muscle relaxant. My legs fall open in a grotesque come-hither manner; my knuckles brush the floor. Whatever is inside – tongue, uvula, moist bubbles of intestinal air – decides to leak out. From time to time, like one of those nodding-duck toys, my head tips forward to empty a quart or so of viscous drool onto my lap, then falls back to begin loading again with a noise like a toilet cistern filling. And I snore, hugely and helplessly, like a cartoon character, with rubbery flapping lips and prolonged, steam-valve exhalations. For long periods I grow unnaturally still, in a way that inclines onlookers to exchange glances and lean forward in concern, then dramatically I stiffen and, after a tantalizing pause, begin to bounce and jostle in a series of whole-body spasms of the sort that bring to mind an electric chair when the switch is thrown. Then I shriek once or twice in a piercing and effeminate manner and wake up to find that all motion within 500 feet has stopped and all children under eight are clutching their mothers' hems. It is a terrible burden to bear.

I have no idea how long I slept in that car other than that it was not a short while. All I know is that when I came to there was a certain heavy silence in the car – the kind of silence that would close over you if you found yourself driving around your own city conveying a slumped and twitching heap from one unperceived landmark to another.

I looked around dumbly, not certain for the moment who these people were, cleared my throat and pulled myself to a more upright position.

"We were wondering if you might like some lunch," my guide said quietly when he saw that I had abandoned for the moment the private ambition to flood his car with saliva.

"That would be very nice," I replied in a small, abject voice.

by Bill Bryson

The Great Gatsby

We walked through a high hallway into a bright rosy-colored space, fragilely bound into the house by French windows at either end. The windows were ajar and gleaming white against the fresh grass outside that seemed to grow a little way into the house. A breeze blew through the room, blew curtains in at one end and out the other like pale flags, twisting them up toward the frosted wedding-cake of the ceiling, and then rippled over the wine-colored rug, making a shadow on it as wind does on the sea.

The only completely stationary object in the room was an enormous couch on which two young women were buoyed up as though upon an anchored balloon. They were both in white, and their dresses were rippling and fluttering as if they had just been blown back in after a short flight around the house. I must have stood for a few moments listening to the whip and snap of the curtains and the groan of a picture on the wall. Then there was a boom as Tom Buchanan shut the rear windows and the caught wind died out about the room, and the curtains and the rugs and the two young women ballooned slowly to the floor.

The younger of the two was a stranger to me. She was extended full length at her end of the divan, completely motionless, and with her chin raised a little, as if she were balancing something on it which was quite likely to fall. If she saw me out of the corner of her eyes she gave no hint of it – indeed, I was almost surprised into murmuring an apology for having disturbed her by coming in.

The other girl, Daisy, made an attempt to rise – she leaned slightly forward with a conscientious expression – then she laughed, an absurd, charming little laugh, and I laughed too and came forward into the room.

Continued ▶

"I'm p-paralyzed with happiness."

She laughed again, as if she said something very witty, and held my hand for a moment, looking up into my face, promising that there was no one in the world she so much wanted to see.

by F Scott Fitzgerald

Level 3 Speaking Verse and Prose

Grade 8 Verse

Prayer Before Birth

I am not yet born; O hear me.
Let not the bloodsucking bat or the rat or the stoat or the
    club-footed ghoul come near me.

I am not yet born, console me.
I fear that the human race may with tall walls wall me,
    with strong drugs dope me, with wise lies lure me,
      on black racks rack me, in blood-baths roll me.

I am not yet born; provide me
With water to dandle me, grass to grow for me, trees to talk
    to me, sky to sing to me, birds and a white light
      in the back of my mind to guide me.

I am not yet born; forgive me
For the sins that in me the world shall commit, my words
    when they speak me, my thoughts when they think me,
      my treason engendered by traitors beyond me,
        my life when they murder by means of my
          hands, my death when they live me.

I am not yet born; rehearse me
In the parts I must play and the cues I must take when
    old men lecture me, bureaucrats hector me, mountains
      frown at me, lovers laugh at me, the white
        waves call me to folly and the desert calls
          me to doom and the beggar refuses
            my gift and my children curse me.

Continued ▶

I am not yet born; O hear me,
Let not the man who is beast or who thinks he is God
    come near me.

I am not yet born; O fill me
With strength against those who would freeze my
    humanity, would dragoon me into a lethal automaton,
      would make me a cog in a machine, a thing with
        one face, a thing, and against all those
          who would dissipate my entirety, would
            blow me like thistledown hither and
              thither or hither and thither
                like water held in the
                  hands would spill me.

Let them not make me a stone and let them not spill me.
Otherwise kill me.

by Louis MacNeice

The Horses

I climbed through woods in the hour-before-dawn dark.
Evil air, a frost-making stillness,

Not a leaf, not a bird –
A world cast in frost. I came out above the wood

Where my breath left tortuous statues in the iron light.
But the valleys were draining the darkness

Till the moorline – blackening dregs of the brightening grey –
Halved the sky ahead. And I saw the horses:

Huge in the dense grey – ten together –
Megalith-still. They breathed, making no move,

With draped manes and tilted hind-hooves,
Making no sound.

I passed: not one snorted or jerked its head.
Grey silent fragments

Of a grey silent world.

I listened in emptiness on the moor-ridge.
The curlew's tear turned its edge on the silence.

Slowly detail leafed from the darkness. Then the sun
Orange, red, red erupted

Silently, and splitting to its core tore and flung cloud,
Shook the gulf open, showed blue,

Continued ▶

And the big planets hanging – .
I turned

Stumbling in the fever of a dream, down towards
The dark woods, from the kindling tops,

And came to the horses.
There, still they stood,
But now steaming and glistening under the flow of light,

Their draped stone manes, their tilted hind-hooves
Stirring under a thaw while all around them

The frost showed its fires. But still they made no sound.
Not one snorted or stamped,

Their hung heads patient as the horizons
High over valleys, in the red levelling rays –

In din of the crowded streets, going among the years, the faces,
May I still meet my memory in so lonely a place

Between the streams and the red clouds, hearing curlews,
Hearing the horizons endure.

by Ted Hughes

On the Frozen Lake

And in the frosty season, when the sun
Was set, and, visible for many a mile
The cottage-windows through the twilight blaz'd,
I heeded not the summons: – happy time
It was, indeed, for all of us; to me
It was a time of rapture: clear, and loud
The village clock toll'd six; I wheel'd about,
Proud and exulting, like an untired horse,
That cares not for his home. – All shod with steel,
We hiss'd along the polish'd ice, in games
Confederate, imitative of the chace
And woodland pleasures, the resounding horn,
The Pack loud bellowing, and the hunted hare.
So through the darkness and the cold we flew,
And not a voice was idle; with the din,
Meanwhile, the precipices rang aloud,
The leafless trees, and every icy crag
Tinkled like iron, while the distant hills
Into the tumult sent an alien sound
Of melancholy, not unnoticed, while the stars,
Eastward, were sparkling clear, and in the west
The orange sky of evening died away.
      Not seldom from the uproar I retired
Into a silent bay, or sportively
Glanced sideway, leaving the tumultuous throng,
To cut across the image of a star
That gleam'd upon the ice: and oftentimes
When we had given our bodies to the wind,

Continued ▸

And all the shadowy banks, on either side,
Came sweeping through the darkness, spinning still
The rapid line of motion; then at once
Have I, reclining back upon my heels,
Stopp'd short; yet still the solitary Cliffs,
Wheeled by me, even as if the earth had roll'd
With visible motion her diurnal round;
Behind me did they stretch in solemn train
Feebler and feebler, and I stood and watch'd
Till all was tranquil as a dreamless sleep.

by William Wordsworth

Portrait of Our Death

There were four of us, following a dirt road which began
in the foothills and went right up into the mountains
where a little cottage was waiting for us. We were driving
slowly, packed in a blue hatchback, and it was getting late

and the rain which had started earlier had begun to really
pelt down. And then, coming round a sharp corner, we lost our grip,
the wheels skidded, wrestling with the thick white rain,
the mud.

The driver, my friend, said "whoa" like you'd say to a horse,
and lifted his hands from the wheel. And I remember
as the car began to spin the mountains turned green,
and as it edged slowly towards the end of the road,

we leaned inward, as you do in films with a car at the edge of a cliff,
watching through the windows, mesmerised, as the valley opened up
in a passionate, open-mouth kiss. We should have tumbled in,
but instead were left unfallen, not yet dead, with the radio still playing.

The driver, my friend, looked green. Our Death was not (as we'd
imagined) the blue car descending the steep gorge-without-ladder,
slipping like a dangerous dress-strap or a crap hand of cards
flung down in disgust. We'd stopped too soon,

left still as rocks, as upturned beetles wriggling their legs,
or the roadside cows chewing slowly. The driver, my friend,
lit a cigarette and sat down. The rain looked on with big cow-eyes.
Not-dying is suddenly being very hungry

Continued ▶

and wet brown shoes caked in mud but not caring
and the mountains feeling slow and the heavy grey clouds
like a washerwoman sprinkling cotton before ironing it flat.
Our Death was pure mathematics –

the steep angle of the cliff which didn't meet the speed of the car –
Our Death was a thing measured in increments, about 66% death
and 33% not-death (just a bit deathy). Probably, we decided,
the mosquitoes in this heat would've sucked us dry

before our death got to us anyway. It was just a slip of the wheels,
we said, a skid, perhaps we'd made too much of its nearness.
Our Death was just a minor character, someone who appeared
about ten miles after a town called River-Without-End, then went on.

And we all felt quite energetic after that. It was hot. It was exciting,
what didn't happen that afternoon. We went hiking
and found a waterfall and fell from it
into deep black pools, lying underneath.

by Katharine Kilalea

Spiritual Chickens

A man eats a chicken every day for lunch,
and each day the ghost of another chicken
joins the crowd in the dining room. If he could
only see them! Hundreds and hundreds of spiritual
chickens, sitting on chairs, tables, covering
the floor, jammed shoulder to shoulder. At last
there is no more space and one of the chickens
is popped back across the spiritual plain to the earthly.
The man is in the process of picking his teeth.
Suddenly there's a chicken at the end of the table,
strutting back and forth, not looking at the man
but knowing he is there, as is the way with chickens.
The man makes a grab for the chicken but his hand
passes right through her. He tries to hit the chicken
with a chair and the chair passes through her.
He calls in his wife but she can see nothing.
This is his own private chicken, even if he
fails to recognise her. How is he to know
this is a chicken he ate seven years ago
on a hot and steamy Wednesday in July,
with a little tarragon, a little sour cream?
The man grows afraid. He runs out of his house
flapping his arms and making peculiar hops
until the authorities take him away for a cure.
Faced with the choice between something odd
in the world or something broken in his head,
he opts for the broken head. Certainly,
this is safer than putting his opinions
in jeopardy. Much better to think he had
imagined it, that he had made it happen.

Continued ▶

Meanwhile, the chicken struts back and forth
at the end of the table. Here she was, jammed in
with the ghosts of six thousand dead hens, when
suddenly she has the whole place to herself.
Even the nervous man has disappeared. If she
had a brain, she would think she had caused it.
She would grow vain, egotistical, she would
look for someone to fight, but being a chicken
she can just enjoy it and make little squawks,
silent to all except the man who ate her,
who is far off banging his head against a wall
like someone trying to repair a leaky vessel,
making certain that nothing unpleasant gets in
or nothing of value falls out. How happy
he would have been to be born a chicken,
to be of good use to his fellow creatures
and rich in companionship after death.
As it is he is constantly being squeezed
between the world and his idea of the world.
Better to have a broken head – why surrender
his corner on truth? – better just to go crazy.

by Stephen Dobyns

Elsewhere

for Stephen Spender

Somewhere a white horse gallops with its mane
plunging round a field whose sticks
are ringed with barbed wire, and men
break stones or bind straw into ricks.

Somewhere women tire of the shawled sea's
weeping, for the fishermen's dories
still go out. It is blue as peace.
Somewhere they're tired of torture stories.

That somewhere there was an arrest.
Somewhere there was a small harvest
of bodies in the truck. Soldiers rest
somewhere by a road, or smoke in a forest.

Somewhere there is the conference rage
at an outrage. Somewhere a page
is torn out, and somehow the foliage
no longer looks like leaves but camouflage.

Somewhere there is a comrade,
a writer lying with his eyes wide open
on mattress ticking, who will not read
this, or write. How to make a pen?

And here we are free for a while, but
elsewhere, in one-third, or one-seventh
of this planet, a summary rifle butt
breaks a skull into the idea of a heaven

Continued ▶

where nothing is free, where blue air
is paper-frail, and whatever we write
will be stamped twice, a blue letter,
its throat slit by the paper knife of the state.

Through these black bars
hollowed faces stare. Fingers
grip the cross bars of these stanzas
and it is here, because somewhere else

their stares fog into oblivion
thinly, like the faceless numbers
that bewilder you in your telephone
diary. Like last year's massacres.

The world is blameless. The darker crime
is to make a career of conscience,
to feel through our own nerves the silent scream
of winter branches, wonders read as signs.

by Derek Walcott

Garden Statues

Between the last night
and the first night...
    a lake of tranquillity...
... ...

Leave that glass of memory to memory –
    let its essence transmute all these nights into gold

Leave the voice of Ali Farka Toure
    soaring
    through the silvered light of that room,
    a room inlaid with the jewels of minutes and hours

Leave your hands lost in the fleeting characters of a keyboard

Leave that wooden rocking-horse
    the old teddy-bear propped on a chair
    the neighbouring gardens

Leave the sun still toying with the sky at eight in the evening

Leave the window open
    on a morning arrayed with morning

Leave that flower labouring to consume you

Leave the peacock emblazoned on a field of beauty

Leave... ... ...

Whatever little time is left
    will never return...

Continued ▶

These jewels cannot return
Thirst will not be slaked by the distant glimpse of a sail

And when you left
   you were burnished,
   you were consumed and yet complete,
   you were fashioned from mother-of-pearl

Then, suddenly, once again,
   you were downcast in clay

Weekdays returned, empty handed
Routine returned

And silence reigned

by Al-Saddiq Al-Raddi,
translated by Sarah Maguire and Sabry Hafez from
the Arabic for the Poetry Translation Centre

A Parental Ode to my Son, Aged Three Years and Five Months

Thou happy, happy elf!
(But stop, – first let me kiss away that tear) –
 Thou tiny image of myself!
(My love, he's poking peas into his ear!)
 Thou merry, laughing sprite!
 With spirits feather-light,
Untouch'd by sorrow and unsoil'd by sin –
(Good heavens! the child is swallowing a pin!)

 Thou little tricksy Puck!
With antic toys so funnily bestuck,
Light as the singing bird that wings the air –
(The door! the door! he'll tumble down the stair!)
 Thou darling of thy sire!
(Why, Jane, he'll set his pinafore a-fire!)
 Thou imp of mirth and joy!
In love's dear chain so strong and bright a link,
Thou idol of thy parents – (Drat the boy!
 There goes my ink!)

 Thou cherub – but of earth;
Fit playfellow for Fays, by moonlight pale,
 In harmless sport and mirth,
(That dog will bite him if he pulls its tail!)
 Thou human humming-bee, extracting honey
From ev'ry blossom in the world that blows,
 Singing in Youth's Elysium ever sunny –
(Another tumble! – that's his precious nose!)

Continued ▶

Thy father's pride and hope!
(He'll break the mirror with that skipping-rope!)
With pure heart newly stamp'd from Nature's mint –
(Where *did* he learn that squint?)
Thou young domestic dove!
(He'll have that jug off, with another shove!)
Dear nursling of the hymeneal nest!
(Are those torn clothes his best?)
Little epitome of man!
(He'll climb upon the table, that's his plan!)
Touch'd with the beauteous tints of dawning life –
(He's got a knife!)

Thou enviable being!
No storms, no clouds, in thy blue sky foreseeing,
Play on, play on,
My elfin John!
Toss the light ball – bestride the stick –
(I knew so many cakes would make him sick!)
With fancies buoyant as the thistledown,
Prompting the face grotesque, and antic brisk,
With many a lamb-like frisk –
(He's got the scissors, snipping at your gown!)

Thou pretty opening rose!
(Go to your mother, child, and wipe your nose!)
Balmy, and breathing music like the South,
(He really brings my heart into my mouth!)
Fresh as the morn, and brilliant as its star, –
(I wish that window had an iron bar!)
Bold as the hawk, yet gentle as the dove –
(I'll tell you what, my love,
I cannot write, unless he's sent above!)

by Thomas Hood

Level 3 Speaking Verse and Prose

Grade 8 Prose

A Thousand Splendid Suns

They stood frozen, Mariam and Laila, eyes to the ground, as though looking at each other would give credence to the way Rasheed saw things, that while he was opening doors and lugging baggage for people who wouldn't spare him a glance a lewd conspiracy was shaping behind his back, in his home, in his beloved son's presence. Neither one of them said a word. They listened to the footsteps in the hallway above, one heavy and foreboding, the other the pattering of a skittish little animal. They listened to muted words passed, a squeaky plea, a curt retort, a door shut, the rattle of a key as it turned. Then one set of footsteps returning, more impatiently now.

Mariam saw his feet pounding the steps as he came down. She saw him pocketing the key, saw his belt, the perforated end wrapped tightly around his knuckles. The fake brass buckle dragged behind him, bouncing on the steps.

She went to stop him, but he shoved her back and blew by her. Without saying a word, he swung the belt at Laila. He did it with such speed that she had no time to retreat or duck, or even raise a protective arm. Laila touched her fingers to her temple, looked at the blood, looked at Rasheed, with astonishment. It lasted only a moment or two, this look of disbelief, before it was replaced by something hateful.

Rasheed swung the belt again.

This time, Laila shielded herself with a forearm and made a grab at the belt. She missed, and Rasheed brought the belt down again. Laila caught it briefly before Rasheed yanked it free and lashed at her again. Then Laila was dashing around the room, and Mariam was screaming words that ran together and imploring Rasheed, as he chased Laila, as he blocked her way and cracked his belt at her. At one point, Laila ducked and managed to land a punch across his ear, which made him spit a curse and pursue her even more relentlessly.

Continued ▸

He caught her, threw her up against the wall, and struck her with the belt again and again, the buckle slamming against her chest, her shoulder, her raised arms, her fingers, drawing blood wherever it struck.

Mariam lost count of how many times the belt cracked, how many pleading words she cried out to Rasheed, how many times she circled around the incoherent tangle of teeth and fists and belt, before she saw fingers clawing at Rasheed's face, chipped nails digging into his jowls and pulling at his hair and scratching his forehead. How long before she realised, with both shock and relish, that the fingers were hers.

He let go of Laila and turned on her.

by Khaled Hosseini

The Forsyte Saga

He had everything in life he wanted – except a little more breath, and less weight – just here! He would see her, when she emerged from the fernery, come, swaying just a little, a violet-grey figure passing over the daisies and dandelions and 'soldiers' on the lawn – the soldiers with their flowery crowns. He would not move, but she would come up to him and say: "Dear Uncle Jolyon, I am sorry!" and sit in the swing and let him look at her and tell her that he had not been very well but was all right now; and that dog would lick her hand. That dog knew his master was fond of her; that dog was a good dog.

It was quite shady under the tree; the sun could not get at him, only make the rest of the world bright so that he could see the Grand Stand at Epsom away out there, very far, and the cows cropping the clover in the field and swishing at the flies with their tails. He smelled the scent of limes, and lavender. Ah! that was why there was such a racket of bees. They were excited – busy, as his heart was busy and excited. Drowsy, too, drowsy and drugged on honey and happiness; as his heart was drugged and drowsy. Summer – summer – they seemed to be saying; great bees and little bees, and the flies too!

The stable clock struck four; in half an hour she would be here. He would have just one tiny nap, because he had had so little sleep of late; and then he would be fresh for her, fresh for youth and beauty, coming towards him across the sunlit lawn – lady in grey! And settling back in his chair he closed his eyes. Some thistledown came on what little air there was, and pitched on his moustache more white than itself. He did not know; but his breathing stirred it, caught there. A ray of sunlight struck through and lodged on his boot. A humble-bee alighted and strolled on the crown of his Panama hat. And the delicious surge of slumber reached the brain beneath that hat, and the head swayed forward and rested on his breast. Summer – summer! So went the hum.

Continued ▸

The stable clock struck the quarter past. The dog Balthasar stretched and looked up at his master. The thistledown no longer moved. The dog placed his chin over the sunlit foot. It did not stir. The dog withdrew his chin quickly, rose, and leaped on old Jolyon's lap, looked in his face, whined; then, leaping down, sat on his haunches, gazing up. And suddenly he uttered a long, long howl.

But the thistledown was still as death, and the face of his old master.

Summer – summer – summer! The soundless footsteps on the grass!

by John Galsworthy

Touching the Void

My torch beam died. The cold had killed the batteries. I saw stars in a dark gap above me. Stars, or lights in my head. The storm was over. The stars were good to see. I was glad to see them again. Old friends come back. They seemed far away; further than I'd ever seen them before. And bright: you'd think them gemstones hanging there, floating in the air above. Some moved, little winking moves, on and off, on and off, floating the brightest sparks of light down to me.

Then, what I had waited for pounced on me. The stars went out, and I fell. Like something come alive, the rope lashed violently against my face and I fell silently, endlessly into nothingness, as if dreaming of falling. I fell fast, faster than thought, and my stomach protested at the swooping speed of it. I swept down, and from far above I saw myself falling and felt nothing. No thoughts, and all fears gone away. So this is it!

A whoomphing impact on my back broke the dream, and the snow engulfed me. I felt cold wetness on my cheeks. I wasn't stopping, and for an instant blinding moment I was frightened. Now, the crevasse! Ahhh… NO!!

The acceleration took me again, mercifully fast, too fast for the scream which died above me…

The whitest flashes burst in my eyes as a terrible impact whipped me into stillness. The flashes continued, bursting electric flashes in my eyes as I heard, but never felt, the air rush from my body. Snow followed down on to me, and I registered its soft blows from far away, hearing it scrape over me in a distant disembodied way. Something in my head seemed to pulse and fade, and the flashes came less frequently. The shock had stunned me so that for an immeasurable time I lay numb, hardly conscious of what had happened. As in dreams, time had slowed, and I seemed motionless in the air, unsupported, without mass. I lay still, with open mouth,

Continued ▶

open eyes staring into blackness, thinking they were closed, and noting every sensation, all the pulsing messages in my body, and did nothing.

I couldn't breathe. I retched. Nothing. Pressure pain in my chest. Retching, and gagging, trying hard for the air. Nothing. I felt a familiar dull roaring sound of shingles on a beach, and relaxed. I shut my eyes, and gave in to grey fading shadows. My chest spasmed, then heaved out, and the roaring in my head suddenly cleared as cold air flowed in.

I was alive.

by Joe Simpson

Lost Horizon

He stumbled to his feet and strode across to the trembling circle of light. The sketch was small, hardly more than a miniature in colored inks, but the artist had contrived to give the flesh-tones a waxwork delicacy of texture. The features were of great beauty, almost girlish in modelling, and Conway found in their winsomeness a curiously personal appeal, even across the barriers of time, death and artifice. But the strangest thing of all was one that he realized only after his first gasp of admiration: the face was that of a young man.

He stammered as he moved away: "But – you said – this was done just before his death?"

"Yes. It is a very good likeness."

"Then if he died in the year you said – "

"He did."

"And he came here, you told me, in 1803, when he was a youth?"

"Yes."

Conway did not answer for a moment: presently, with an effort, he collected himself to say: "And he was killed, you were telling me?"

"Yes. An Englishman shot him. It was a few weeks after the Englishman had arrived at Shangri-La. He was another of those explorers."

"What was the cause of it?"

"There had been a quarrel – about some porters. Henschell had just told him of the important proviso that governs our reception of guests. It was a task of some difficulty, and ever since, despite my own enfeeblement, I have felt constrained to perform it myself."

Continued ▶

The High Lama made another and longer pause, with just a hint of enquiry in his silence; when he continued, it was to add: "Perhaps you are wondering, my dear Conway, what that proviso may be?"

Conway answered slowly and in a low voice: "I think I can already guess."

"Can you, indeed? And can you guess anything else after this long and curious story of mine?"

Conway dizzied in brain as he sought to answer the question; the room was now a whorl of shadows with that ancient benignity at its center. Throughout the narrative he had listened with an intentness that had perhaps shielded him from realizing the fullest implications of it all. Now, with the mere attempt at conscious expression, he was flooded over with amazement, and the gathering certainty in his mind was almost stifled as it sprang to words.

"It seems impossible," he stammered. "And yet I can't help thinking of it – it's astonishing – and extraordinary – and quite incredible – and yet not *absolutely* beyond my powers of belief – "

"What is, my son?"

And Conway answered, shaken with an emotion for which he knew no reason and which he did not seek to conceal: *"That you are still alive, Father Perrault."*

by James Hilton

The Quiet American

The two men watched us – I write men, but I doubt whether they had accumulated forty years between them. "And these?" Pyle asked, and he added with a shocking directness, "Shall I shoot them?" Perhaps he wanted to try the sten.

"They've done nothing."

"They were going to hand us over."

"Why not?" I said. "We've no business here. It's their country."

I unloaded the rifle and laid it on the floor. "Surely you're not leaving that," he said.

"I'm too old to run with a rifle. And this isn't my war. Come on."

It wasn't my war, but I wished those others in the dark knew that as well. I blew the oil-lamp out and dangled my legs over the trap, feeling for the ladder. I could hear the guards whispering to each other like crooners, in their language like a song. "Make straight ahead," I told Pyle, "aim for the rice. Remember there's water – I don't know how deep. Ready?"

"Yes."

"Thanks for the company."

"Always a pleasure," Pyle said.

I heard the guards moving behind us: I wondered if they had knives. The megaphone voice spoke peremptorily as though offering a last chance. Something shifted softly in the dark below us, but it might have been a rat. I hesitated. "I wish to God I had a drink," I whispered.

"Let's go."

Continued ▸

Something was coming up the ladder: I heard nothing, but the ladder shook under my feet.

"What's keeping you?" Pyle said.

I don't know why I thought of it as something, that silent stealthy approach. Only a man could climb a ladder, and yet I couldn't think of it as a man like myself – it was as though an animal were moving in to kill, very quietly and certainly with the remorselessness of another kind of creation. The ladder shook and shook and I imagined I saw its eyes glaring upwards. Suddenly I could bear it no longer and I jumped, and there was nothing there at all but the spongy ground, which took my ankle and twisted it as a hand might have done. I could hear Pyle coming down the ladder; I realized I had been a frightened fool who could not recognize his own trembling, and I had believed I was tough and unimaginative, all that a truthful observer and reporter should be. I got on my feet and nearly fell again with the pain. I started out for the field dragging one foot after me and heard Pyle coming behind me. Then the bazooka shell burst on the tower and I was on my face again.

by Graham Greene

Blueeyedboy

The colour of murder is blue, he thinks. Ice-blue, smokescreen blue, frostbite, post-mortem, body-bag blue. It is also *his* colour in so many ways, running through his circuitry like an electrical charge, screaming blue murder all the way.

Blue colours everything. He sees it, senses it everywhere, from the blue of his computer screen to the blue of the veins on the backs of her hands, raised now and twisted like the tracks of sandworms on Blackpool beach – where they used to go, the four of them, every year on his birthday, and he would have an ice-cream cone, and paddle in the sea, and search out the little scuttling crabs from under the piles of seaweed, and drop them into his bucket to die in the heat of the simmering birthday sun.

Today he is only four years old, and there is a peculiar innocence in the way he carries out these small and guiltless slayings. There is no malice in the act, merely a keen curiosity for the scuttling thing that tries to escape, sidling round and round the base of the blue plastic bucket; then, hours later, giving up the fight, claws splayed, and turning its vivid underbelly upwards in a futile show of surrender, by which time he has long since lost interest and is eating a coffee ice cream (a sophisticated choice for such a little boy, but vanilla has never been his taste), so that when he rediscovers it at the end of the day, when the time comes to empty his bucket and to go home, he is vaguely surprised to find the creature dead, and wonders, indeed, how such a thing could ever have been alive at all.

His mother finds him wide-eyed on the sand, poking the dead thing with a fingertip. Her main concern is not for the fact that her son is a killer, but for the fact that he is suggestible, and that many things upset him in a way that she does not understand.

Continued ▸

"Don't play with that," she tells him. "It's nasty. Come away from there."

"Why?" he says.

Good question. The creatures in the bucket have been standing undisturbed all day. He gives it some thought. "They're dead," he concludes. "I collected them all, and now they're dead."

His mother scoops him into her arms. This is precisely what she dreads. Some kind of outburst: tears, perhaps; something that will make the other mothers look down their noses at her and sneer.

She comforts him. "It's not your fault. It was just an accident. Not your fault."

An accident, he thinks to himself. Already, he knows that this is a lie.

by Joanne Harris

The Cat's Table

There was a shudder during dessert as the boat's engines started. We all got up and went out to the railings to watch the departure, our castle slipping away slowly from the thin horizon of lights, back into the great darkness.

We guarded the dog that night. He was fearful of our sudden movements, until Ramadhin managed to bring him into his bunk and fall asleep with his arms around him. When the three of us woke the next morning we had already entered the Red Sea, and it was during this passage, on the first day steaming north, that something astonishing happened.

It had always been difficult to penetrate the barrier that separated us from First Class. Two polite and determined stewards either let you through or turned you away. But even they could not stop Ramadhin's small dog. He had leapt out of Cassius's arms and bolted from the cabin. We ran up and down the empty hallways looking for him. Within moments the little fellow must have emerged into the sunlight of B Deck and run beside the railings, raced perhaps into the lower ballroom, up its gilded staircase, and past the two stewards into First Class. They managed to grab him, but soon he was free again. He had eaten none of the food we had offered him, which we'd smuggled out of the dining room in our trouser pockets, so perhaps he was looking for something to eat.

No one was able to corner him. Passengers saw him for just a blurred moment. He did not seem at all interested in humans. Well-dressed women crouched down, calling out high-pitched, artificial-sounding greetings, but he charged past them all without a pause and into the cherrywood cave of the library, and disappeared somewhere beyond that. Who could know what he was after? Or what he was feeling, in that no doubt pounding heart? He was just a hungry or scared dog on this claustrophobic ship whose alleyways

Continued ▶

suddenly became cul-de-sacs, as he ran farther and farther from any sign of daylight. Eventually the creature made his way trotting along a mahogany-panelled, carpeted hall and slipped through a half-open door into a master suite, as someone left it carrying a full tray. The dog jumped up onto an oversized bed, where Sir Hector de Silva lay, and bit down into his throat.

by Michael Ondaatje

The Pickwick Papers

From the centre of the ceiling of this kitchen, old Wardle had just suspended, with his own hands, a huge branch of mistletoe, and this same branch of mistletoe instantaneously gave rise to a scene of general and delightful struggling and confusion; in the midst of which, Mr Pickwick, with a gallantry that would have done honour to a descendant of Lady Tollimglower herself, took the old lady by the hand, led her beneath the mystic branch, and saluted her in all courtesy and decorum. The old lady submitted to this piece of practical politeness with all the dignity which befitted so important and serious a solemnity, but the younger ladies, not being so thoroughly imbued with a superstitious veneration for the custom; or imagining that the value of a salute is very much enhanced if it cost a little trouble to obtain it: screamed and struggled, and ran into corners, and threatened and remonstrated, and did everything but leave the room, until some of the less adventurous gentlemen were on the point of desisting, when they all at once found it useless to resist any longer, and submitted to be kissed with a good grace. Mr Winkle kissed the young lady with the black eyes, and Mr Snodgrass kissed Emily, and Mr Weller, not being particular about the form of being under the mistletoe, kissed Emma and the other female servants, just as he caught them. As to the poor relations, they kissed everybody, not even excepting the plainer portions of the young-lady visitors, who, in their excessive confusion, ran right under the mistletoe, as soon as it was hung up, without knowing it! Wardle stood with his back to the fire, surveying the whole scene, with the utmost satisfaction; and the fat boy took the opportunity of appropriating to his own use, and summarily devouring, a particularly fine mince-pie, that had been carefully put by for somebody else.

by Charles Dickens

Publication Details

Prose Selections

Level 1 – Grade 2

Mr Gum and the Cherry Tree by Andy Stanton,
Egmont Books Ltd (ISBN: 9781405252188)

Alana Dancing Star: Samba Spectacular by Arlene Phillips,
Faber and Faber (ISBN: 9780571259892)

Through the Looking-Glass by Lewis Carroll,
HarperCollins (ISBN: 978000735093)

Tumtum and Nutmeg: A Circus Adventure by Emily Bearn,
Egmont Books Ltd (ISBN: 9781405254441)

Fantastic Mr Fox by Roald Dahl,
Puffin (ISBN: 9780141322650)

I Don't Believe It, Archie! by Andrew Norriss,
David Fickling Books (ISBN: 9781849920803)

The Wombles by Elisabeth Beresford,
Bloomsbury Publishing PLC (ISBN: 9781408808375)

William in Trouble by Richmal Crompton,
Macmillan Children's Books (ISBN: 9780330544719)

Level 1 – Grade 3

Coraline by Neil Gaiman,
Bloomsbury Publishing PLC (ISBN: 9780747562108)

Victory by Susan Cooper,
Corgi Childrens (ISBN: 9780552554152)

The London Eye Mystery by Siobhan Dowd,
David Fickling Books (ISBN: 9781849920445)

The White Giraffe by Lauren St John,
Orion Childrens (ISBN: 9781842555637)

The Sheep-Pig by Dick King-Smith,
Puffin (ISBN: 9780141333366)

A Girl Called Dog by Nicola Davies,
   Corgi Childrens (ISBN: 9780552563017)

How To Be a Pirate by Cressida Cowell,
   Hodder Children's Books (ISBN: 9780340999080)

Born To Run by Michael Morpurgo,
   HarperCollins Children's Books (ISBN: 9780007230594)

Level 2 – Grade 4

The Roman Mysteries: The Secrets of Vesuvius by Caroline Lawrence,
   Orion Childrens (ISBN: 9781842550212)

The Wolves of Willoughby Chase by Joan Aiken,
   Red Fox (ISBN: 9780099456636)

The Sleeping Army by Francesca Simon,
   Profile Books (ISBN: 9781846682797)

Little Women by Louisa May Alcott,
   Vintage (ISBN: 9780099572961)

A Medal for Leroy by Michael Morpurgo,
   HarperCollins Children's Books (ISBN: 9780007487516)

Half Moon Investigations by Eoin Colfer,
   Puffin (ISBN: 9780141320809)

When You Reach Me by Rebecca Stead,
   Andersen (ISBN: 9781849392129)

Girl, Missing by Sophie McKenzie,
   Simon & Schuster (ISBN: 9780857074133)

Level 2 – Grade 5

Macbeth (Shakespeare Stories) by Leon Garfield,
   Puffin (ISBN: 9780140389388)

I Shall Wear Midnight by Terry Pratchett,
   Corgi Childrens (ISBN: 9780552166058)

The Adventure of the Speckled Band (The Adventures of Sherlock Holmes) by Sir Arthur Conan Doyle,
   BBC Books (ISBN: 9781849903677)

The Wheel of Surya by Jamila Gavin,
Egmont Books Ltd (ISBN: 9780749747442)

Pride and Prejudice by Jane Austen,
Wordsworth Editions Ltd (ISBN: 9781853260001)

The Vanished by Celia Rees,
Marion Lloyd Books (ISBN: 9781407110608)

Eating Things On Sticks by Anne Fine,
Yearling (ISBN: 9780440869375)

Virals by Kathy Reichs,
Arrow (ISBN: 9780099544579)

Level 3 – Grade 6

Refugee Boy by Benjamin Zephaniah,
Bloomsbury Publishing PLC (ISBN: 9780747550860)

Ithaka by Adèle Geras,
Corgi Childrens (ISBN: 9780552547994)

The Toymaker by Jeremy de Quidt,
David Fickling Books (ISBN: 9781849920049)

Stalking Ivory by Suzanne Arruda,
Piatkus (ISBN: 9780749953362)

No Great Mischief by Alistair MacLeod,
Vintage (ISBN: 9780099283928)

The Hunger Games by Suzanne Collins,
Scholastic (ISBN: 9781407109084)

The Thirty-Nine Steps by John Buchan,
Vintage Classics (ISBN: 9780099528395)

Nicholas Nickleby by Charles Dickens,
Penguin (ISBN: 9780141199818)

Level 3 – Grade 7

Brave New World by Aldous Huxley,
Vintage (ISBN: 9780099518471)

The Shadow of the Sun by Ryszard Kapuściński,
Penguin (ISBN: 9780140292626)

The Double Comfort Safari Club by Alexander McCall Smith,
Abacus (ISBN: 9780349119991)

Trespass by Rose Tremain,
Vintage (ISBN: 9780099478454)

Dot Robot: Cyber Gold by Jason Bradbury,
Puffin (ISBN: 9780141323978)

Jamaica Inn by Daphne Du Maurier,
Virago (ISBN: 9781844080397)

Down Under by Bill Bryson,
Black Swan (ISBN: 9780552997034)

The Great Gatsby by F Scott Fitzgerald,
Wordsworth Editions Ltd (ISBN: 9781853260414)

Level 3 – Grade 8

A Thousand Splendid Suns by Khaled Hosseini,
Bloomsbury Publishing PLC (ISBN: 9780747585893)

The Forsyte Saga by John Galsworthy,
Wordsworth Editions Ltd (ISBN: 9781840224382)

Touching the Void by Joe Simpson,
Vintage (ISBN: 9780099771012)

Lost Horizon by James Hilton,
Summersdale Publishers (ISBN: 9781840243536)

The Quiet American by Graham Greene,
Vintage (ISBN: 9780099478393)

Blueeyedboy by Joanne Harris,
Black Swan (ISBN: 9780552773164)

The Cat's Table by Michael Ondaatje,
Vintage (ISBN: 9780099554424)

The Pickwick Papers by Charles Dickens,
Wordsworth Editions Ltd (ISBN: 9781853260520)

Author Index

Acknowledgements

For permission to reprint the copyright material in the anthology we make grateful acknowledgement to the following authors, publishers and executors:

Adams, Kate *The Cheering Rain* Used by permission of Kate Adams **Aiken, Joan** From *The Wolves of Willoughby Chase* by Joan Aiken (Copyright © Joan Aiken). Reprinted by permission of A M Heath & Co Ltd **Al-Qasim, Samih** *The Clock on the Wall* Translated by Nazih Kassis. Used by permission of Ibis Editions **Al-Raddi, Al-Saddiq** *Garden Statues* Translated from the Arabic by Sarah Maguire and Sabry Hafez for The Poetry Translation Centre. Used by permission of The Poetry Translation Centre **Andrew, Moira** *Snake* Used by permission of Moira Andrew **Arruda, Suzanne** From *Stalking Ivory* by Suzanne Arruda. Published by Little, Brown Book Group (World excluding US and Canada); copyright © 2006 by Suzanne Arruda. Used by permission of Dutton Signet, a division of Penguin Group USA Inc (US and Canada) **Aykroyd, Clarissa** *Andalucía* and *London, 7 July* Used by permission of Clarissa Aykroyd **Bearn, Emily** From *Tumtum and Nutmeg: A Circus Adventure* by Emily Bearn. Text copyright © Emily Bearn 2008. Published by Egmont UK Ltd London and used with permission of Egmont and A P Watt Ltd **Belloc, Hilaire** *The Vulture* From *More Beasts For Worse Children* by Hilaire Belloc. Reprinted by permission of Peters Fraser & Dunlop (www.petersfraserdunlop.com) on behalf of the Estate of Hilaire Belloc **Beresford, Elisabeth** From *The Wombles* © Elisabeth Beresford, 2010, Bloomsbury Publishing PLC **Betjeman, John** *Hunter Trials* © John Betjeman by permission of The Estate of John Betjeman **Bloom, Valerie** *Chicken Poxed* © Valerie Bloom 2000, from *Let Me Touch the Sky*, reprinted by permission of Valerie Bloom **Bradbury, Jason** From *Dot Robot: Cyber Gold* by Jason Bradbury (Puffin Books, 2011). Text copyright © Jason Bradbury, 2011 **Brown, Palmer** *The Spangled Pandemonium* Used by permission of Palmer Brown **Bruchac, Joseph** *Birdfoot's Grampa* Used by permission of Barbara S Kouts **Bryson, Bill** From *Down Under* by Bill Bryson. Published by Black Swan. Reprinted by permission of The Random House Group Ltd and the author **Causley, Charles** *Colonel Fazackerley* From *I Had a Little Cat*, published by Macmillan. Used by permission of David Higham Associates **Chatterjee, Debjani** *My Sari* Used by permission of Debjani Chatterjee **Chattopadhyaya, Harindranath** *Peacock* Used by permission of B R Publishing Corporation **Chisholm, Alison** *Sunday Tea* Used by permission of Alison Chisholm **Coghill, Nevill** Translation of *The Canterbury Tales* by Geoffrey Chaucer. Reproduced with permission of Curtis Brown Group Ltd, London on behalf of the Estate of Nevill Coghill. Copyright © Nevill Coghill, 1951 **Colfer, Eoin** From *Half Moon Investigations* by Eoin Colfer. Text copyright © 2006 by Eoin Colfer. Used by permission of Penguin Books Ltd (World excluding US and Canada); reprinted by permission of Disney-Hyperion Books, an imprint of Disney Book Group, LLC.

All rights reserved (US and Canada) **Collett, Andrew** *Chinese New Year in Chinatown* © Evan-Moor Corporation **Collins, Suzanne** Excerpt from *The Hunger Games* by Suzanne Collins. Copyright © 2008 by Suzanne Collins. Published by Scholastic Press, an imprint of Scholastic Inc. Reprinted by permission of Scholastic Inc **Cookson, Paul** *Where Teachers Keep Their Pets* Used by permission of Paul Cookson **Cooper, Susan** From *Victory* by Susan Cooper. Published by Bodley Head. Reprinted by permission of The Random House Group Limited (World excluding US); reprinted with the permission of Margaret K McElderry Books, an imprint of Simon & Schuster Children's Publishing Division. Copyright © 2006 Susan Cooper (US) **Cope, Wendy** *Huff* Reprinted by permission of United Agents on behalf of Wendy Cope **Cowell, Cressida** From *How To Be a Pirate* by Cressida Cowell, first published in the UK by Hodder Children's, an imprint of Hachette Children's Books, 338 Euston Road, London NW1 3BH **Crompton, Richmal** Excerpt from *William in Trouble* by Richmal Crompton. Copyright © Macmillan Children's Books 2011 **Cunliffe, John** *The Mutinous Jack-in-the-box* Used by permission of David Higham Associates **Dahl, Roald** From *Fantastic Mr Fox* by Roald Dahl, copyright © 1970 by Roald Dahl Nominee Limited, copyright renewed 1998 by Felicity Dahl, Chantal Sophia Dahl, Theo Dahl, Ophelia Dahl, and Lucy Faircloth Dahl. Used by permission of Alfred A Knopf, an imprint of Random House Children's Books, a division of Random House, Inc. Any third party use of this material, outside of this publication, is prohibited. Interested parties must apply directly to Random House, Inc for permission (US). Used by permission of David Higham Associates (World excluding US) **Davies, Nicola** From *A Girl Called Dog* published by Corgi Childrens, Random House Group Limited. Used by permission of David Higham Associates **De Quidt, Jeremy** From *The Toymaker* by Jeremy de Quidt. Published by David Fickling. Reprinted by permission of The Random House Group Limited (World excluding US); Text copyright © 2008 by Jeremy de Quidt. Used by permission of David Fickling Books, an imprint of Random House Children's Books, a division of Random House, Inc. Any third party use of this material, outside of this publication, is prohibited. Interested parties must apply directly to Random House, Inc. for permission (US) **Dobyns, Stephen** *Spiritual Chickens* From *Velocities* published by Bloodaxe Books. Used by permission of David Higham Associates **Dowd, Siobhan** From *The London Eye Mystery* by Siobhan Dowd. Published by David Fickling. Reprinted by permission of The Random House Group Limited (World excluding US); copyright © 2007 by Siobhan Dowd. Used by permission of David Fickling Books, an imprint of Random House Children's Books, a division of Random House, Inc. Any third party use of this material, outside of this publication, is prohibited. Interested parties must apply directly to Random House, Inc for permission (US) **Duffy, Carol Ann** *Backstage* Copyright © Carol Ann Duffy. Reproduced by permission of the author c/o Rogers, Coleridge & White Ltd, 20 Powis Mews, London W11 1JN **Du Maurier, Daphne** From *Jamaica Inn* by Daphne Du Maurier. Reproduced with permission of Curtis Brown Ltd, London, on behalf of The Chichester Partnership. Copyright © Daphne Du Maurier 1936 **Edwards, Richard** *The*

Estate of Ted Hughes. Used by permission of Faber and Faber Ltd (World excluding US/Canada); reprinted by permission of Farrar, Straus and Giroux, LLC (US/Canada) **Huxley, Aldous** From *Brave New World* by Aldous Huxley. Published by Vintage Books. Reprinted by permission of The Random House Group Limited (World excluding US and Canada); copyright 1932, renewed © 1960 by Aldous Huxley. Reprinted by permission of HarperCollins Publishers (US); reprinted by permission of Random House Canada (Canada) **Joseph, Jenny** *Warning* Copyright © Jenny Joseph, from *Selected Poems*, Bloodaxe Books 1992. Reproduced with permission of Johnson & Alcock Ltd **Kapuściński, Ryszard** From *The Shadow of the Sun* by Ryszard Kapuściński, translated by Klara Glowczewska, copyright © 2001 by Klara Glowczewska (Allen Lane The Penguin Press, 2001). Copyright © Ryszard Kapuściński, 2001 (British Commonwealth, Australia and New Zealand). Used by permission of Alfred A Knopf, a division of Random House, Inc. Any third party use of this material, outside of this publication, is prohibited. Interested parties must apply directly to Random House, Inc for permission (Rest of World) **Khalvati, Mimi** *Rubaiyat* Used by permission of Carcanet Press Limited **Kilalea, Katharine** *Portrait of Our Death* Used by permission of Carcanet Press Limited **King-Smith, Dick** From *The Sheep-Pig* by Dick King-Smith (Puffin, 1983). Copyright © Dick King-Smith 1983 (British Commonwealth, Australia and New Zealand). Used by permission of A P Watt at United Agents, on behalf of Fox Busters Ltd (Rest of World) **Kirkup, James** *High Dive* Used by permission of The James Kirkup Collection **Laura** *I Am* Used by permission of Bullying UK **Lawrence, Caroline** From *The Roman Mysteries: The Secrets of Vesuvius* published by Orion Children's Books (an imprint of the Orion Publishing Group, London). Copyright © Caroline Lawrence, 2001 **Lees, Joan** *Flight* Used by permission of Joan Lees **Leighton, Patricia** *Night Spinner* Used by permission of Patricia Leighton **Lister, Daphne** *The Sea* Used by permission of Daphne Lister **MacCaig, Norman** *Small Boy* from *Collected Poems* by Norman MacCaig is reproduced by permission of Polygon, an imprint of Birlinn Ltd (www.birlinn.co.uk) **McCall Smith, Alexander** Excerpt from *The Double Comfort Safari Club* by Alexander McCall Smith, published by Abacus. Used by permission of David Higham Associates **McGough, Roger** *What She Did* and *The Cats' Protection League* from *Bad Bad Cats* by Roger McGough © 1997, Viking-Penguin Books Ltd reprinted by permission of Peters Fraser & Dunlop (www.petersfraserdunlop.com) on behalf of Roger McGough **McKenzie, Sophie** Extract from *Girl, Missing* by Sophie McKenzie (Copyright © Sophie McKenzie) is reproduced by permission of United Agents (www.unitedagents.co.uk) on behalf of Sophie McKenzie (World excluding UK and Commonwealth) **Macleod, Alistair** From *No Great Mischief* by Alistair Macleod. Published by Jonathan Cape. Reprinted by permission of The Random House Group Ltd (UK and Commonwealth excluding Canada); reprinted by permission of McClelland & Stewart (Canada); copyright © 1999 by Alistair Macleod. Used by permission of W W Norton & Company, Inc (US) **McLeod, Eleanor** *Ballet Lesson* Used by permission of Eleanor McLeod. From *More Poems for Children to Enjoy and Teachers Too*

Wear Midnight: A Discworld Novel by Terry Pratchett. Published by Doubleday. Reprinted by permission of The Random House Group Ltd (World excluding US); copyright © 2010 by Terry Pratchett. Used by permission of HarperCollins Publishers (US) **Prelutsky, Jack** *Be Glad Your Nose Is on Your Face* Used by permission of HarperCollins Publishers **Prévert, Jacques** *Breakfast* Translated by Lawrence Ferlinghetti. Reprinted by permission of City Lights Books **Rees, Celia** From *The Vanished*. Text copyright © Celia Rees, 1997. Reproduced by permission of Scholastic Ltd. All rights reserved **Reichs, Kathy** From *Virals* by Kathy Reichs. Published by Young Arrow. Reprinted by permission of The Random House Group Limited (UK and Commonwealth); copyright © 2010 by Kathy Reichs. Used by permission of Razorbill, A Division of Penguin Young Readers Group, A Member of Penguin Group (USA) Inc (Rest of World) **Rich, Adrienne** *Aunt Jennifer's Tigers* Copyright © 2002, 1951 by Adrienne Rich, from *The Fact of a Doorframe: Selected Poems 1950–2001* by Adrienne Rich. Used by permission of W W Norton & Company, Inc **Rumble, Coral** *The First Bit* From *Breaking the Rules* (2004), published by Lion Children's Books. Used by permission of Coral Rumble **St John, Lauren** From *The White Giraffe*, published by Orion Children's Books (an imprint of the Orion Publishing Group, London) © Lauren St John, 2006 **Sassoon, Siegfried** *Everyone Sang* Copyright Siegfried Sassoon, by kind permission of the Estate of Siegfried Sassoon **Semple, Hilary** *Patel's Shop: Indian Bazaar* Used by permission of Hilary Semple **Seraillier, Ian** *The Visitor* From *A Second Poetry Book*, Oxford University Press, ed John Foster, 0199181373, 1980. © Estate of Ian Seraillier **Siddique, John** *Haikus of the Seasons* Used by permission of John Siddique **Silverstein, Shel** *Zebra Question* From *A Light in the Attic* by Shel Silverstein. © 1981 Evil Eye Music, Inc. By permission of Edite Kroll Literary Agency Inc **Simon, Francesca** From *The Sleeping Army*. Used by permission of Profile Books and Faber and Faber Ltd **Simpson, Joe** From *Touching the Void* by Joe Simpson. Published by Jonathan Cape. Reprinted by permission of The Random House Group Limited (World excluding US); copyright © 1989 by Joe Simpson. Reprinted by permission of HarperCollins Publishers (US) **Stanton, Andy** From *Mr Gum and the Cherry Tree* by Andy Stanton. Text copyright © Andy Stanton 2007. Published by Egmont UK Ltd London and used with permission **Stead, Rebecca** From *When You Reach Me* by Rebecca Stead, copyright © 2009 by Rebecca Stead. Used by permission of Wendy Lamb Books, an imprint of Random House Children's Books, a division of Random House, Inc. Any third party use of this material, outside of this publication, is prohibited. Interested parties must apply directly to Random House, Inc for permission **Stevens, Roger** *Farewell, Pete* From *Why Otters Don't Wear Socks*. Used by permission of Macmillan Children's Books **Szirtes, George** *In the Land of Giants* and translation *of Winter Trees* by Zoltán Zelk. Used by permission of George Szirtes. From *In the Land of the Giants* by George Szirtes (Salt Publishing, 2012) **Tessimond, A S J** *Jamaican Bus Ride* Used by permission of Whiteknights Press at University of Reading **Thiele, Colin** *Hamburgers* Used by permission of Triple D Books **Tremain, Rose** From *Trespass* by Rose Tremain. Published by Chatto & Windus. Reprinted